MODERN MATHEMATICS

MODERN MATHEMATICS

Introductory Concepts and their Implications

A.B. Evenson

Visiting Instructor, Faculty of Education, University of Alberta — General Supervisor, Senior High Schools, Edmonton, Alberta — Co-author, Canadian edition of *Seeing Through Mathematics*

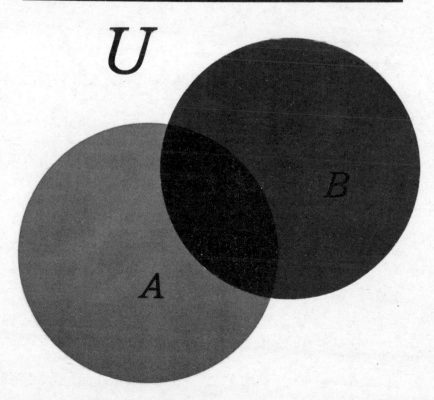

SCOTT, FORESMAN AND COMPANY
CHICAGO ATLANTA DALLAS PALO ALTO FAIRLAWN, N.J.

PREFACE

The purpose of this book is to give the reader an insight into the nature of "the new" or modern mathematics. Each topic has been discussed on an elementary level with a sincere attempt to preserve accuracy of mathematical expression. In other words, the book offers a first exposure or orientation to modern mathematics. It is not directed toward the student of advanced mathematics. Interested readers will find several good references for further study at the end of each chapter.

There is no intention on the part of the writer to determine policy, outline a program, or suggest the most suitable content or methodology for school mathematics. The ultimate place of modern mathematics in school programs will be decided only after much study and experimentation, involving students, teachers of mathematics, and school administrators.

Many mathematicians claim that our school programs in mathematics are out-of-date and in need of improvement through a more modern and fundamental approach. Because the world of today needs more mathematicians and demands more from them, it follows that all of us who have responsibilities for mathematics in the schools should examine with care the recent and significant developments in this major field of knowledge.

A. B. E.

CONTENTS

---

[1] A Bibliography appears at the end of each chapter.
[2] Problems for Review follow this and subsequent chapters.

SYMBOLS

$=$	equals
$\neq$	does not equal
$\wedge$	and
$\vee$	or
$\rightarrow$	if . . ., then . . .
$\leftrightarrow$	if and only if
$\sim$	not
$>$	is greater than
$<$	is less than
$\geq$	is greater than or equal to
$\leq$	is less than or equal to
$\lvert a \rvert$	absolute value of a
$\subseteq$	is included in, inclusion
$\subset$	is a proper subset of
(x, y)	coordinates of a point in the plane
$\equiv$	is congruent to
$\cap$	intersection
$\cup$	union
$\bar{A}$	complement of set A
ϕ	null set, or empty set
$\in$	is an element of
$\notin$	is not an element of
$\vert$	such that, or satisfying the condition that
F^i	inverse of the function F
R^i	inverse of the relation R

1 WHAT IS MODERN MATHEMATICS?

There is much discussion of modern mathematics among educators today. Perhaps "modern mathematics" is an unfortunate choice of term because of its connotations. Some people may feel it implies that mathematics was never modern before. Others may infer that traditional mathematics no longer has anything to offer. Neither viewpoint is justified. Generally speaking, modern mathematics is the mathematics which is presently being developed and applied, with special significance for the second half of the twentieth century.

The purpose of this chapter is to present the point of view of modern mathematics. First we shall discuss a few general characteristics of modern mathematics; for further clarification we shall examine some specific characteristics of modern mathematics, and then we shall relate them in a general way to the school program.

An understanding of modern mathematics will emerge from the reading of this book as a whole rather than from the study of any individual chapter. Nevertheless, this brief introduction will direct attention to the purpose of the book and set the stage for the implications which are drawn in the final chapter. At that point, one may find profit in a second reading of Chapter 1.

SOME GENERAL CHARACTERISTICS

The Role of Postulates

In the past, mathematics has often been regarded as a tool subject. Now it is becoming evident that mathematics is much more than that, although most people still hold to the narrower concept of the subject. This point of view may lead us to forget that mathematics is man-made and, therefore, neither infallible nor immutable. Furthermore, it may suggest a reason why we continue to rely on mathematical ideas that were discovered hundreds of years ago, without recognizing the need to look for new concepts. Unfortunately, it also obscures the real power and beauty of the subject.

We may have been taught that mathematics is a static science, whose eternal truth serves all purposes. For example, we learned that parallel lines do not intersect, and that the sum of the interior angles of a triangle is 180°. Actually, the truth of these statements depends upon the postulates we accept. In other words, the theorems we develop depend upon the agreements we make initially. These include certain undefined terms and postulates.

The understanding many people have concerning the nature of definitions is perhaps another reason for the development of stereotyped notions about mathematics. Somehow, most students believe that every word can be defined, and no doubt they will be disturbed to learn this is not true. In building a deductive system, it is necessary to select a number of concepts that are undefined, such as "point" and "line", and to define other concepts in terms of them.

Deductive proof, which is given greater emphasis in the new mathematics, is based on undefined terms and postulates. A deductive system consists of undefined terms, postulates, and theorems that are shown to be true on the basis of the postulates through the application of the laws of logic. If we start from new and different postulates, we can formulate new theorems.

No doubt many people believe that all progress in science is based on experimental evidence and observation. To a limited degree this is true; nevertheless, many scientific theories originated in postulational methods. For example, the molecular theory arose in this manner and gained acceptance by yielding satisfactory predictions of many physical phenomena. From all this, we do not wish to imply that experimental evidence and observation are unimportant in scientific development. We simply wish to point out that complete dependence on empirical methods would impose serious limitations on scientific progress.

Modern mathematics is moving farther away from the physical world although it offers many new and practical applications. That is to say, mathematics is becoming more abstract. Considerable mathematics is being developed with no specific application in mind. To many persons this would seem to be a useless type of activity but, strangely enough, it often proves fruitful. There are instances in which a great scientist like Einstein has picked up some mathematics which was developed without thought of application, and used it to formulate a new physical theory.

In summary, we may say that less reliance is being placed on what has been regarded as self-evident truth, and that greater emphasis is being given to the exploration of systems based upon postulates. Especially in higher mathematics, two characteristics of modern thought are abandonment of the idea that there exists one set of axioms or postulates that are self-evident, and acceptance of increased dependence on postulational methods.

The Notion or Concept of Set

Several new areas in mathematics have come into prominence recently. We call them new because they have not been included in school programs, not because they were developed last year or last month. Actually, study of some "new" areas of mathematics began many years ago. For example, the algebra of sets is attributed to George Boole, who died in 1864. The first publication on the theory of games appeared in 1928 in an article written by John Von Neumann. The theory of games has found many important applications in business and military strategy during the past ten years. About the turn of the century, David Hilbert, a German mathematician, corrected serious gaps in the geometry developed by Euclid two thousand years ago.

Some mathematicians believe that the most significant single innovation in their field in the last hundred years is the theory of sets, the development of which is largely due to the work of another German mathematician, Georg Cantor (1845–1918). For the most part, set theory is too advanced for high school mathematics. However, the notion or concept of set can be used to advantage to clarify and unify other mathematical concepts such as cardinal number, variable, and relation. Any set theory that might be included in a secondary school program would be of an elementary nature, for example, the algebra of sets.

Logic and Methodology

The nature of a logical system is the key to methodology in modern mathematics. Mathematical proof demands a special type of reasoning known as logical deduction. The mathematician does not, and feels he cannot, say that this or that is true, but commences a proof by some statement such as "If p is true, then q is true". From this, the proof is derived through logic. Logic therefore is an important element in mathematics because it governs the pattern of deductive proof through which mathematics is developed. The use of logic in mathematics is not new, but during the last sixty or seventy years there has been a greater emphasis on the analysis of logical structure of mathematics as a whole.

Mathematical Structure or Pattern

Certain fundamental ideas in mathematics occur and recur. These give rise to basic structures or patterns which help to integrate and strengthen mathematical ideas. It may be said that the development of new mathematics is essentially a search for new patterns. We have briefly discussed deductive proof. As we study methods of proof we shall find consistent patterns that will prove helpful. In Chapter 3 we shall attempt to show that number systems have a definite structure that facilitates their use in problem solving. In Chapter 5 we shall point out a common pattern of all relations. For all mathematics, learning and application are facilitated by the discovery of common patterns and generalizations. These features are emphasized in the new mathematics; they were given much less significance in traditional or classical mathematics.

Recently mathematics has found greater application in economics, psychology, and the social and biological sciences. Much of the work in these areas has helped to emphasize the importance of mathematical structure and patterns. In addition, much of the new mathematics developed for these areas has proved useful in the study of mathematics itself.

SOME SPECIFIC CHARACTERISTICS OF MODERN MATHEMATICS RELATED TO A SCHOOL PROGRAM IN MATHEMATICS

Unification and Integration of Mathematical Ideas and Procedures

We shall find that some of the patterns to which we have referred earlier are common to arithmetic, algebra, and geometry, which suggests a closer integration of these areas. In fact, separate treatments of the various branches of mathematics become more difficult and even inadvisable in a modern approach to the subject. The emphasis on mathematical structure implies many changes. It suggests that increased emphasis must be given to such basic principles and patterns as those inherent in number and numeration systems, and to the properties of operations from which we abstract generalizations. All of these are integrated by such unifying concepts as the notion of a set, the notion of a number system, the notion of a mathematical condition, and the notion of a relation.

Continuity of Sequence and Experience

The total program in mathematics should provide for continuity of experience and sequence of topics. For example, the concept of number cannot be allocated to certain grades. It must be a feature of mathematics that unfolds gradually, step by step, from Grade 1 to Grade 12. In most school programs of mathematics there is a lack of continuity. This is especially evident in mathematics programs of the higher grades. It is difficult to establish continuity when we place geometry in one compartment and algebra in another, and at the same time show very little concern for the order in which they are taught. When we do this, we jeopardize the framework of a logical and sequential development.

More Precise Definitions, Terminology, and Notation

Everyone knows that modern science has had considerable influence on our everyday vocabulary. Many words that we accept and use did not exist a few years ago, e.g., transistors, orlon, pliofilm, borazon, and sputnik. One might expect that in mathematics, too, new terminology is being developed. In the study of modern mathematics, we observe that many familiar definitions have been replaced by new ones that are more precise. Some new symbols and notation also have been introduced.

In this new mathematics, considerable time should be taken to get acquainted with what we may call the language of mathematics. Many mathematicians believe that the student's progress in this subject is often retarded because of his inability to verbalize accurately and concisely. In many cases this is not the fault of the student, but rather the fault of carelessly prepared materials.

In the past, many of our definitions have not been precise. This is due in part to the fact that traditional mathematics emphasized the use of rules instead of the formation of mathematical concepts. In modern mathematics increased attention is given to precision of statement. In modern mathematics we do not speak of a "line" when we mean "line segment". We do not say "the line AB is six inches" when we mean that "the measure of the line segment AB is six inches". We do not define an angle as "the amount of turning or rotation in a plane about a point", but as "a figure or configuration formed by two rays with a common end point". Instead of defining square root as "one of two equal factors of a number", we say that the square root of a number x, $x \geq 0$, is that non-negative number a, such that $a^2 = x$. Instead of defining absolute value as the value of a signed number when its sign is omitted, we say that *the absolute value of x, written* $|x|$, *equals x if $x \geq 0$, or $-x$ if $x < 0$.* (See page vi for meanings of symbols used above.)

Distinction between Objects and Names of Objects

Another characteristic of modern mathematics is the careful distinction made between objects and names of objects. Many implications for school mathematics arise from this characteristic. For example, in considering numbers, it is important to maintain the distinction between numbers and numerals (names for numbers). This distinction in turn forces us to consider other distinctions such as the distinction between a statement and a sentence.

We shall not give other examples here as they would be difficult to comprehend out of context. However, modern mathematics differentiates sharply between the names of objects or ideas and the objects or ideas themselves.

Emphasis on Deductive Proof

Mathematics has always aimed at the development of the student's ability to reason, but the typical program has fallen short in its contribution toward this end. A student should have an opportunity to develop his reasoning power by the frequent use of inductive and deductive methods. Most students will have had some understanding of the inductive method from their experience with its use in the physical sciences. Induction is that type of reasoning in which a general conclusion is reached on the basis of facts obtained through a systematic examination of many instances that, in some respects, are alike. Much of geometry can be enlivened and made more challenging by frequent use of the inductive or "discovery" method. Students should be cautioned, however, not to rely completely on methods of induction. Although certain relationships found to be present in a number of samples may lead to a generalization, sometimes that generalization may prove false for a larger sample.

Much of the new advanced mathematics has been developed through deductive techniques. Since this process is based on postulates (assumptions), it is often referred to as postulational thinking. For centuries the axioms of Euclid were regarded as self-evident truths. This point of view was destroyed by several mathematicians, including Lobachevsky and Bolyai in their work in geometry just over one hundred and fifty years ago. They showed conclusively that these "self-evident truths" must be regarded as assumptions (statements that are accepted without proof). As a result, increased emphasis has been placed on deductive reasoning in algebra as well as in geometry, because each is seen to be based on a set of assumptions.

It is an interesting fact that certain generalizations discovered inductively are later used as postulates in deductive proof. For example, early in the elementary school a child discovers that $a + b = b + a$, and accepts this as a generalization. However, in later grades he will regard $a + b = b + a$ as a postulate and use it as such in deductive proof. Still later he may learn to prove that $a + b = b + a$, basing his proof upon the assumptions of set theory or upon a set of postulates such as the Peano postulates.

Emphasis on Problem Solving

All of the foregoing implications should have a tremendous impact on problem solving at all levels. Before a problem can be solved by mathematical methods it must be translated into mathematical symbols. Therefore, students must have a clear and complete understanding of all the mathematical symbols they need to use. Finally, they must be skilled in computational processes through understanding of mathematical techniques and adequate related practice.

In this age of rapid change, careful attention must be given to sound problem-solving techniques. We cannot hope to teach children how to solve all the various problems they may encounter, so we must be sure to teach the basic principles of mathematics and of problem solving in order that students may apply them correctly in varying situations.

WHY ARE CHANGES BEING PROPOSED NOW?

Some people may question why so many changes in mathematics are being proposed just now. No doubt many other questions will arise in the minds of people on learning of modern mathematics for the first time. Why is there a revolution in mathematics? Why did the new ideas for improving mathematics not come along gradually? Why is so much attention being given now to school mathematics?

There are many reasons for the current revolution in mathematics:

1. The applications of mathematics have increased considerably in recent years. Its use has penetrated not only into the physical sciences but

8 ❋

also into the biological and social sciences, and into all branches of technology, business, and industry.

2. The need for new and more powerful mathematics has resulted in the creation and use of new areas of mathematics.

3. Among mathematicians, the natural outcome of this extension was recognition of the inadequacies of traditional mathematics and, in many instances, the search for ways to improve traditional programs.

There are good reasons why many feel that modern mathematics should have considerable impact on school mathematics. As a result, much attention has been given to this problem.

1. The development of the new mathematics has raised serious questions as to the traditional mathematics programs of the schools. Many feel there is a possibility that modern mathematics may be easier to learn and that perhaps students can learn more mathematics in less time. There is also the possibility that students who fail in traditional programs may do well in a modern program. We must find out.

2. After a half century of neglect, we find top mathematicians and public school educators co-operating more than ever before to improve the school mathematics program. Their intent is to provide a sequential program for the entire school.

3. As this modern movement in mathematics has caught the fancy of the public, financial assistance has been provided to enable interested mathematicians and educators to give sufficient time and effort to the improvement of school programs in mathematics.

4. At the present time the climate of opinion is favorable toward improvement in mathematics. The reasons for this, at least in part, are the shortage of mathematicians to meet present needs, and the feeling that many students, who experience difficulty in mathematics, would welcome a fresh approach.

BIBLIOGRAPHY

1. *Program for College Preparatory Mathematics.* Commission on Mathematics. New York: College Entrance Examination Board, 1959.
2. *Appendices.* Commission on Mathematics. New York: College Entrance Examination Board, 1959.
3. *Modernizing the Mathematics Curriculum.* Commission on Mathematics. New York: College Entrance Examination Board, 1958.
4. *New Developments in Secondary-school Mathematics.* National Council of Teachers of Mathematics. 1201 Sixteenth Street N.W., Washington 6, D.C. 1959.
5. *The Secondary Mathematics Curriculum.* National Council of Teachers of Mathematics. 1201 Sixteenth Street N.W., Washington 6, D.C. Reprinted.

2 SETS

SET MEMBERSHIP

The word *set* is synonymous with *collection* or *class*. A mathematics club, the set of natural numbers, a collection of books in a library, a class of students, are all examples of sets. The individual persons, numbers, or objects in a set are known as the *members* or *elements* of the set.

We shall not attempt to define set. We shall use it as a primitive or undefined term to define other terms. If we are given an object, we can decide whether it belongs or does not belong to the set. The members or elements belonging to a set are determined by the distinguishing characteristics of the set. For example, consider all the books in a library as a set. Each book in the library may be, in some respects, different from or similar to all other books in the library. However, the property we are using here to form a set is the fact that the book is in the library. This gives us a well-defined collection of objects as we are able to determine whether or not any given object is a member of our set. To indicate set membership, we use the symbol $\in$; non-membership is indicated by $\notin$. The symbol $\in$ is read "is an element of", and the symbol $\notin$ is read "is not an element of".

Suppose *The Call of the Wild* is a book in the library but the book *Little Women* is not a book in the library. If we denote the set of books in the library as A, *The Call of the Wild* as a, and *Little Women* as b, we could express these facts in the following abbreviated form:

$$a \in A, \quad \text{and} \quad b \notin A.$$

These are read, "*The Call of the Wild* is an element of the set of books in the library", and "*Little Women* is not an element of the set of books in the library".

Note that throughout this book we shall use capital letters to denote sets. When small letters are used, they will denote members or elements of sets.

In mathematics, the word *set* refers to a *collection of definite, distinct objects of our perception or of our thought*. In the next chapter we shall discuss sets of numbers. An example of such a set is the set of numbers one through six. The members of this set are abstract ideas. These ideas have names. We use the numerals 1, 2, 3, 4, 5, 6 to name these ideas. When we see the symbol {1, 2, 3, 4, 5, 6}, we should think about the set of numbers one through six. Observe that we use braces to indicate that certain objects are elements of a set.

SPECIFYING A SET

On many occasions it is possible to specify a set by simply listing the names of all its members. This method of specifying a set is called *tabulation*. *To specify a set by tabulation, we simply list the names of the members between braces* { }. The braces are used to denote the total membership of a set and are read "the set whose members are". Suppose the members of a relay team are John, Bill, Jim, and Bob. This set could be specified as follows: {John, Bill, Jim, Bob}. This would be read "the set whose members are John, Bill, Jim, Bob". Following are some further examples of specifying a set by tabulation:

1. {0, 1, 2}.

This is read "the set whose members are zero, one, two". The order of tabulating the names of the members of a set is immaterial. This same set could be tabulated as {1, 0, 2} or {2, 1, 0}. Remember that the symbol {0, 1, 2} is a name for a set of numbers. The numerals between the braces are names for the numbers. Thus, we can say that {0, 1, 2} = {1, 0, 2} = {2, 1, 0}.

2. {January, February, March, April, May, June, July, August, September, October, November, December}.

This is read "the set whose members are January, February, March, April, May, June, July, August, September, October, November, December".

Most of the sets considered in mathematics have so many members that it would be inadvisable, inconvenient, and sometimes impossible to indicate total membership by tabulation. Sets of this type are specified by *description* or *rule*. *To specify a set by these methods, either we must give a name that denotes the set, or we must give a rule that indicates the requirements for membership in the set.* Following are examples of specifying a set by description: the human race; the animal kingdom; the set of natural numbers; the set of even numbers less than 100; the set of all odd numbers;

the set of natural numbers each of which has 3 as a factor; the set of all natural numbers up to, but not including, 1000.

It should be clear that the sets that were specified by tabulation in examples 1 and 2, could also be specified by description as follows:

1. The first three natural numbers, and
2. The months of the year.

It is not always possible to tabulate a set that is specified by description. For example, the set of rational numbers cannot be tabulated because it is an infinite set.

UNIVERSE: FINITE AND INFINITE SETS

The set of things or objects under consideration in a discussion is often referred to as the *universe of discourse* or simply the *universe*, denoted by *U*. The notion of a universe is very important in mathematics. In Chapter 4 this new idea will be explained more fully.

Each set has subsets. *A is a subset of B, if each member of A is also a member of B.* For example, in the set of all reindeer, there is a subset whose members are male reindeer. When a subset has no members we call it the empty or null set and denote it by $\{\}$ or ϕ. (It is important to remember that the empty set is a subset of any set.) In the set of "all reindeer" we could consider the set of elephants. Since the universe of discourse is "all reindeer" there are no members that are elephants. Therefore we say that the set of elephants in this universe is "empty" or is the "empty set".

Now suppose our universe of discourse or universe is the set of natural numbers. In this universe, the set of natural numbers less than ten is a subset. The set of natural numbers less than zero is also a subset of the set of natural numbers but, since there are no natural numbers less than zero, this subset is "empty".

A set is finite if it is empty or if it can be counted by a natural number. A set may, of course, have only one member or element. The following are finite sets: the set of players on a baseball team (nine); the set of catchers on a baseball team (one); the set of quarterbacks on a baseball team (zero); the set of the provinces of Canada; the set of residents of Chicago; the set of natural numbers less than one hundred; the set of integers between -1 and $+1$ (one).

A set is infinite if it is not finite. Examples of infinite sets are the set of rational numbers and the set of points in a line.

RELATIONS BETWEEN SETS

Relations between sets can be represented by means of Venn diagrams. A Venn diagram is a plane figure in which sets can be represented geometrically by letting points of the plane represent the members of the universe (*U*). The region bounded by any plane figure can be used for such symbolic representation of a set, but it is customary to use the region bounded by a rectangle. Subsets are usually represented by disks within the rectangle. For example, if the universe (*U*) is "all horses", and set *A* "all race horses", this relationship can be illustrated by the following Venn diagram:

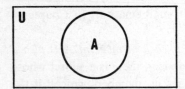

Fig. 1

Suppose *B* denotes "all horses that are completely black" and *C* denotes "all horses that are completely white". This relationship is shown in Figure 2.

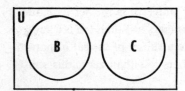

Fig. 2

In this case no horse is a member of both sets, and we say that *B* and *C* are *disjoint* sets. *A and B are disjoint if no member of A is a member of B.*

Other examples of disjoint sets are the set of bicycles and the set of motor cars, the set of positive integers and the set of negative integers.

If we let *A* denote "all race horses" and *B* denote "all black horses", the Venn diagram for this relationship would be as shown in Figure 3.

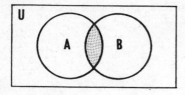

Fig. 3

Because some race horses are black, there are some horses that are members of both sets *A* and *B* (shaded area). In such instances, we say that set *A meets* set *B* or simply that "*A meets B*". For the generalization of this relationship we say that *A meets B whenever some members of A are also members of B*. Examples are the set of blonde co-eds and the set of blue-eyed co-eds (some blonde co-eds are also blue-eyed), and the set of all baseball players and the set of all hockey players (some hockey players are also baseball players).

For *A* and *B* it can happen that all members of *A* are also members of *B*. For example, if *A* is the set of positive integers and *B* is the set of all integers, *A* is a subset of *B*. Or we may say that *A* is *included* in *B*. The symbol for inclusion is ($\subseteq$). Therefore this relationship can be expressed as $A \subseteq B$. The diagram for this relationship is shown in Figure 4.

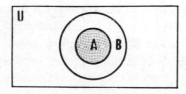

Fig. 4

Some additional examples of inclusion are as follows: (1) the set of rectangles is included in the set of quadrilaterals, (2) the set of property owners is included in the set of people in a city. We may write the generalization for $A \subseteq B$ as follows: *A is included in B whenever all members of A are also members of B*.

We can have the relationship, $A = B$, where $A \subseteq B$ and $B \subseteq A$. Suppose that *A* is "the boys in the Grade 12 class" and *B* is "the members of the Grade 12 basketball team". If all the Grade 12 boys make up the entire basketball team, then each member of *A* is a member of *B* and each member of *B* is a member of *A*. Therefore, we say that *A* and *B* are equal sets or that $A = B$. In a Venn diagram for this special relationship, the disk representing one set will cover exactly and completely the disk representing the second set as shown in Figure 5. The universe (U) here can be all the the boys in the high school.

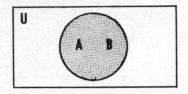

Fig. 5

The generalization of this relationship follows: *A equals B when all members of A are members of B and also all members of B are members of A.*

We have said that if every member of A is also a member of B, A is included in B ($A \subseteq B$). We also say that if every member of A is included in B, then A is called a subset of B. According to this definition a set can be a subset of itself and can be equal to the set of which it is a subset. A subset that does not equal the set is called a *proper subset* of the set. *A is a proper subset of B if A $\subseteq$ B and A $\neq$ B.* When A is a proper subset of B, we write $A \subset B$ or $B \supset A$, which is read "A is a proper subset of B" or "B properly includes A".

EXAMPLE: Let the universe (U) be the natural numbers one through ten, $A = \{1, 2, 3\}$ and $B = \{1, 2, 3, 4, 5\}$. Each member of A is included in B, and therefore A is a subset of B. But A is not equal to B. Therefore A is a *proper subset* of B. In the same universe, suppose $A = \{1, 2, 3, 4\}$ and $B = \{1, 2, 3, 4\}$. Then each member of A is included in B, and therefore A is a subset of B. But A is equal to B. Consequently A is not a proper subset of B. In fact, $A = B$.

OPERATIONS ON SETS

Two of the operations on sets are operations on two sets to produce one new set. Such operations are called *binary* operations. Addition and multiplication are binary operations on numbers since they assign single numbers to pairs of numbers.

Intersection

We shall now consider the *intersection* of two sets, which is formed by a binary operation. *If A and B are two sets, we can form a new set consisting of just those elements that belong to both A and B. This new set is called the intersection of A and B, and is denoted by the symbol A ∩ B.* This is commonly read, "*A* cap *B*". It is illustrated by the Venn diagram in Figure 6.

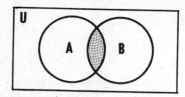

Fig. 6

EXAMPLE: Given the universe (*U*) as all male college students,

A = all male college freshmen,
B = all male college students over six feet tall.

The Venn diagram of this relationship would be the same as Figure 6 and A ∩ B (shaded area) would be the college freshmen over six feet tall.

The four examples that follow are special cases of intersection, A ∩ B. In each example the following descriptions apply:

U = all college students,
A = all college freshmen,
B = all college students over six feet tall.

(*a*) If all college freshmen are over six feet tall, the Venn diagram will be as in Figure 7.

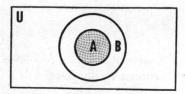

Fig. 7

(*b*) If all college students over six feet tall are freshmen, the Venn diagram will be as in Figure 8.

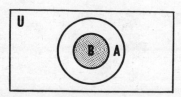

Fig. 8

(c) If all college freshmen are over six feet tall and all college students over six feet tall are freshmen, the Venn diagram will be as in Figure 9.

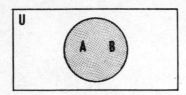

Fig. 9

(d) If no college freshman is over six feet tall, the Venn diagram will be as in Figure 10.

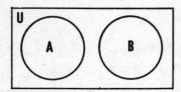

Fig. 10

Since by definition the set $A \cap B$ contains just those members that belong to both A and B, and since in this example there are no such members, $A \cap B = \phi$ (the empty set).

Let us consider two examples using natural numbers.

EXAMPLE 1:
$$U = \{1, 2, 3, 4, 5, 6, 7, 8\}.$$
$$A = \{2, 3, 4\}.$$
$$B = \{6, 7, 8\}.$$
$$A \cap B = \phi \text{ (the empty set)}.$$

The Venn diagram for $A \cap B$ will be like the one for Figure 10. Since we know what the Venn diagram will be, let us choose to illustrate $A \cap B$ by the use of number lines. See Figure 11.

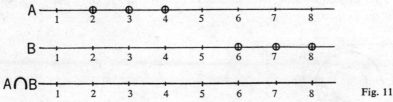

Fig. 11

$A \cap B = \phi$, since A and B are disjoint.

EXAMPLE 2:
$$U = \{1, 2, 3, 4, 5, 6, 7, 8, 9, 10\}.$$
$$A = \{1, 2, 3, 4, 5, 6\}.$$
$$B = \{5, 6, 7, 8\}.$$

$A \cap B = \{5, 6\}$ because this set contains just those members that belong to both A and B.

The Venn diagram for this example will be the same as Figure 6 (A meets B). The number line diagram is in Figure 12.

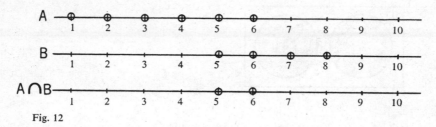

Fig. 12

Union

Here we have another binary operation on sets. *If A and B are two sets, we can form a new set consisting of just those elements that belong either to A or to B or to both A and B. This new set is called the union of A and B,* and is denoted by the symbol $A \cup B$. This is commonly read "A cup B".

EXAMPLES:
(a) $U = \{$Bob, James, John, Peter, Harry, Bill, Joe, Tim, Frank$\}$.
$A = \{$James, John, Peter$\}$.
$B = \{$Bob, James, Harry, John$\}$.

Then $A \cup B = \{$Bob, James, John, Peter, Harry$\}$, because these five boys are just those boys who belong either to A or to B or to both. The Venn diagram for this operation will be as in Figure 13. Observe that A meets B because James and John are members of both sets. It should be understood, however, that James and John are not included twice in the set $A \cup B$.

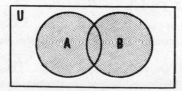

Fig. 13

(b) $U = $ {Bob, James, John, Peter, Harry, Bill, Joe, Tim, Frank}.
$A = $ {John, Peter, James}.
$B = $ {Harry, Bill, Joe}.

Then $A \cup B = $ {John, Peter, James, Harry, Bill, Joe} because these six boys are just those boys who belong to A or to B or to both A and B. The Venn diagram will be as in Figure 14. Observe that A and B are disjoint because no member of A is a member of B.

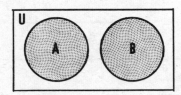

Fig. 14

(c) $U = $ {6, 7, 8, 9, 10, 11, 12, 13, 14, 15}.
$A = $ {8, 9, 10, 11, 12}.
$B = $ {10, 11, 12, 13, 14, 15}.

Then $A \cup B = $ {8, 9, 10, 11, 12, 13, 14, 15} (A meets B). The Venn diagram will be as in Figure 13. The number line illustration is shown in Figure 15. $A \cup B = $ {8, 9, 10, 11, 12, 13, 14, 15}, because this is the set that contains just those members that belong either to A or to B or to both.

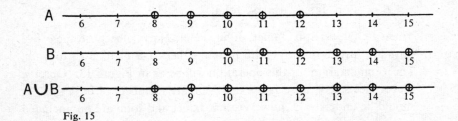

Fig. 15

(d) $U = $ {6, 7, 8, 9, 10, 11, 12, 13, 14, 15}.
$A = $ {8, 9, 10}.
$B = $ {14, 15}.

Then $A \cup B = $ {8, 9, 10, 14, 15} (A and B are disjoint). The Venn diagram is shown in Figure 14. The number line illustration is shown in Figure 16. $A \cup B = \{8, 9, 10, 14, 15\}$, because this is the set that contains just those members that belong either to A or to B.

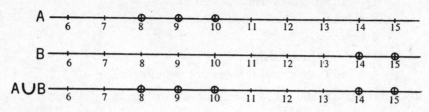

Fig. 16

The following Venn diagrams illustrate special cases of $A \cup B$.

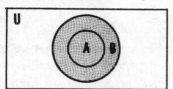

Fig. 17

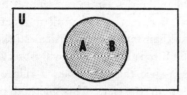

Fig. 18

Complement

Not all operations are binary. We can have an operation that acts on a single set to produce another set. *If A is a set, then the set of just those things in the universe that do not belong to A is known as the complement of A.* It may be symbolized by $\bar{A}$, which is read "the complement of A". It is also common practice to denote the complement of A by A' or $\sim A$. In Figure 19, the shaded area is $\bar{A}$, the complement of A.

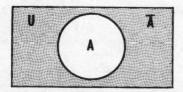

Fig. 19

EXAMPLES:

(a) $U = $ {all high school students}.

$\quad A = $ {all male high school students}.

$\quad \bar{A} = $ {all female high school students}.

(b) $U = $ {all angles}.

$\quad A = $ {all right angles}.

$\quad \bar{A} = $ {all those angles that are not right angles}.

Both examples (a) and (b) can be illustrated by Fig. 19.

STANDARD DESCRIPTION OF SETS

Earlier in this chapter we learned that when we tabulate a set we use braces to stand for "the set whose members are". When we describe a set we can also use braces to stand for these words. Suppose we are given the sentence $x < 10$. This expresses the condition that each member of the solution set is less than 10. We can symbolize the description of the set by writing $\{x | x < 10\}$. This is read "the set of all x (or the set of all numbers specified by the universe) such that x is less than ten". The vertical stroke (|) is read "such that" or "satisfying the condition that". You will observe that the vertical stroke is followed by a sentence that expresses a rule or condition under which x gains membership in the set. This method of describing a set is known as a standard description of a set.

Finally, let us use this method for describing the new sets formed under the operations of intersection, union, and complement as follows:

(a) $A \cap B = \{x \mid x$ is a member of A *and* x is a member of $B\}$.
This is read

the set of all x, such that

x is a member of set A *and*

x is a member of set B.

By "and" we mean that x is a member of both A and B.

(b) $A \cup B = \{x \mid x$ is a member of A *or* x is a member of $B\}$.
This is read

the set of all x, such that

x is a member of set A *or*

x is a member of set B.

The "or" here means that x is a member of A or B, or x is a member of both A and B.

(c) $\bar{A} = \{x \mid x \text{ is } not \text{ a member of } A\}$.
This is read

the set of all x, such that
x is *not* a member of A.

APPLICATIONS AND USES OF SETS

Having established the language and meaning of relations and operations with sets, you will find that it is not difficult to use them in a logical development of mathematics. You will observe that the notion of sets threads through all the remaining chapters, and that it helps to clarify and simplify many traditional mathematical concepts. It should become evident that the concept of set is not wholly separate from other areas of mathematics, but that it actually permeates and integrates many mathematical topics. Because the notion of set is so useful and because, as we said, it is a powerful unifying concept, we have given it early treatment in this book.

PROBLEMS FOR REVIEW

1. (*a*) Give three examples of specifying a set by description or rule.
   (*b*) Give three examples of specifying a set by tabulation.

2. Give three examples of infinite sets not mentioned in Chapter 2.

3. Make up sets (use capital letters to denote sets) of continents so that
   (*a*) A is a proper subset of B.
   (*b*) $B = C$.
   (*c*) $D = \phi$.

4. Draw Venn diagrams to illustrate the following:
   (*a*) A is disjoint from B, and $B \subseteq C$.
   (*b*) A meets B, B meets C, and A is disjoint from C.
   (*c*) $B = C$.

5. Tabulate all possible subsets of $\{a, b, c, d\}$.

6. Suppose our universe is all houses, and that A is the set of all two-storey houses and B is the set of all houses built in 1952:

   (a) Describe in words the set of houses specified by each of the following:

   i. $A \cap B$ iv. $\bar{B}$

   ii. $A \cup B$ v. $\overline{A \cap B}$

   iii. $\bar{A}$ vi. $\overline{A \cup B}$

   (b) Interpret the following sentences:

   i. A meets B.   iii. A is disjoint from B.

   ii. $A \subseteq B$.   iv. A equals B.

7. If $U = \{1, 2, 3, 4, 5, 6, 7, 8\}$,
   $A = \{2, 3, 4\}$,
   $B = \{4, 5, 6, 7\}$,
   determine the sets $A \cup B$ and $A \cap B$ by means of Venn diagrams and number lines.

BIBLIOGRAPHY

1. ALLENDOERFER, C. G. and OAKLEY, C. O. *Principles of Mathematics*. New York: McGraw-Hill Book Company, 1955.

2. CHRISTIAN, ROBERT, R. *Introduction to Logic and Sets*. Toronto, Ontario: Ginn and Company, 1958.

3. KRICKENBERGER and PEARSON. *Sets and the Structure of Algebra*. Toronto, Ontario: Ginn and Company, 1958.

4. MCSHANE, E. J. "Operating with Sets", Chapter III: *Insights into Modern Mathematics*. 23rd Yearbook of the National Council of Teachers of Mathematics.

5. *Sentences, Sets*. Mathematics Staff of the College. University of Chicago Press, 1956.

3 NUMBER AND NUMERATION

MEANING OF NUMBER

The history of number is interwoven with the history of mankind because of the strong relationship between man's ability to handle numbers and his control of the world about him. But what do we mean by number? It is both convenient and useful to define number in terms of *sets*.

Before we can define the concept of number in terms of sets, we must understand the idea of a *one-to-one correspondence*. This concept is of crucial importance in mathematics. Early man used the concept of one-to-one correspondence to keep track of his sheep. He did this by matching (laying aside) one pebble for each animal. Mathematically, we describe this situation by stating that the set of pebbles is in one-to-one correspondence with the set of sheep. This means that for each pebble there is one and only one sheep and for each sheep there is one and only one pebble. Let us define the concept of one-to-one correspondence:

> *Two sets, A and B, are said to be in one-to-one correspondence when we have a matching, or pairing, of the elements of A with the elements of B such that each element of A corresponds to one and only one element of B and each element of B corresponds to one and only one element of A.*

Consider, for example, the sets

$$A = \{1, 2, 3\} \quad \text{and}$$
$$B = \{a, b, c\}.$$

One way of placing these sets in one-to-one correspondence is as follows:

$$
\begin{array}{ccc}
1 & 2 & 3 \\
\updownarrow & \updownarrow & \updownarrow \\
a & b & c
\end{array}
$$

Now let us use one-to-one correspondence to develop the meaning of number. Suppose we consider a set of three plates, a set of three chairs, a set of three people, a set of three apples, and a set of three knives. What is common to all these sets? Obviously, these sets have in common the same *number* of members, namely three. The concept of number remains when we disregard the nature of the members of a set.

Thus numbers appear as properties of sets. *Two sets that can be placed in one-to-one correspondence are said to be equivalent.* Equivalent sets have the same number. Thus the set {x, y, s, u, v} has the same number as the set of fingers on one hand, namely *five*. By proceeding in this way, we can develop the concept of number. In other words, we develop the meaning represented by each of the symbols 1, 2, 3, 4, 5 . . ..

Numbers can be *ordered*. Let us consider the following two sets and their associated numbers:

$$\{a, b, c\}, \quad \{a, b, c, d\},$$
$$3 \quad , \quad 4$$

We observe that the first set can be placed in a one-to-one correspondence with a proper subset of the second set:

$$\{a, b, c\}$$
$$\{a, b, c, d\}.$$

This leads us to infer that the first set has fewer members than the second set. Therefore we can say that 3 is less than 4 and so write the sentence $3 < 4$. (The symbol ($<$) is read, "is less than".)

By using many other examples, we can develop the following:

$$0 < 1 < 2 < 3 < 4 < 5 < 6 . . ..$$

Zero is less than each of the other cardinal numbers. We can think of cardinal zero as the number of elements in a set that has no elements. As we mentioned in Chapter 2, the set with no elements is commonly called the empty set. In other words, zero is associated with the empty set.

It now appears that we have sufficient information to discuss the process of counting. It will be easier to do this if we have a prior understanding of what is known as a *standard set*. In the previous discussion, we used the set {a, b, c}. This set is equivalent to {'1', '2', '3'}.* All sets equivalent to {'1', '2', '3'} have three members. Similarly, all sets equivalent to {'1'} have

* Single quotation marks here indicate that we mean numeral, not number. As a general rule, single quotation marks indicate that we are talking about the name rather than the thing itself. Thus {'1', '2', '3'} is a set of names or numerals and not a set of numbers.

one member and all sets equivalent to {'1', '2'} have two members. These sets of names are known as *standard sets*. The last member of each standard set is the name of the cardinal number of the set.

Notice that the members of standard sets are written in order, that is, they are *ordered*. For example, the standard set {'1', '2', '3', '4'} is named by the numeral 4. With respect to this standard set we would also say that it has four members and that any set equivalent to this set has four members. When we count, we actually find the standard set that is equivalent to the set of objects to be counted. That is to say, the set of objects to be counted is put into one-to-one correspondence with a standard set. For example, if the set of objects to be counted can be put into one-to-one correspondence with the standard set {'1', '2', '3', '4', '5', '6'}, the number of objects in one set is six since we have agreed that the last member of our standard set is the name of the number of members in the set. In fact, it is the name for the cardinal number of all sets equivalent to it.

We have learned that cardinal numbers are numbers that are used to answer the question "how many?" or, more correctly, "how many members are in this set?" In some instances we are not interested in the number of members in a set, but in the position that a member of the set may hold. For example, if we have six desks in a row and a student occupying each desk, we may wish to know what position a particular student has in this row. If Mary Adams is sitting at a desk which corresponds to the numeral 5 in the standard set that represents the row of desks, we could say that she is sitting at Desk 5 or at the 5th desk. "5th" is an example of an *ordinal* number, or the ordinal use of number, as it refers to the position in line of a single student. Let us cite more examples of these two special uses of number:

1. The office building is 12 stories high (*cardinal* use); the president's office is on the 10th floor (*ordinal* use).

2. The stairway has 18 steps (*cardinal* use); Johnny is sitting on the 14th step (*ordinal* use).

In this brief section we have developed two meanings of number. Next, we shall consider systems for naming the numbers.

MEANING OF NUMERATION

The purpose of a *system of numeration* is to provide a systematic method of naming the numbers. By numeration, we mean the use of number symbols or numerals to represent numbers. It is important that we distinguish between *number* and *numeral*.

Words are symbols for things and not the actual things. For example, we cannot put a house on the chalkboard but we can write 'house', which is simply a symbol. Similarly, we cannot write the number 4 on the chalkboard but we can write the symbol 4 on the chalkboard. In other words, we can write the number symbol or numeral, but we cannot write a number.

SYSTEMS OF NUMERATION

The system of numeration that we use has a very interesting historical background. Before studying it, let us look briefly at some older systems of numeration.

The Roman System

Most of us have some acquaintance with the Roman system of numeration because Roman numerals have always been included in our arithmetic program and because we continue to use Roman numerals for various purposes. Some of the basic Roman symbols with their numeral equivalents in our system are as follows: I, 1; V, 5; X, 10; L, 50; C, 100; D, 500; M, 1000. In many ways the Roman system is cumbersome, particularly in computation. First, it frequently uses many symbols to name a number. For example, it uses six symbols (XLVIII) to name 48. Second, it uses more than one base. In some instances numbers are related to 5 and are made by subtracting or adding units, for example, the numbers named by the symbols IV and VI. Again, other numbers are related to 10 by adding and subtracting units, e.g., the numbers named by the symbols IX and XI. The same is true for the numbers grouped around fifty, one hundred, five hundred, etc. In other words, the Romans did not have a single base as we have, and as certain other ancient civilizations had.

The Babylonian System

By 1600 B.C. the Babylonians had developed quite an efficient system of numeration. The numerals were composed of wedge-shaped marks written on clay tablets with a stylus. Following are examples of Babylonian numerals with equivalent numerals in our base ten system:

V, 1; VVVVV, 5; ◄, 10; ◄◄, 20; ◄◄◄VV, 32

Observation of these numerals and a further study of the Babylonian system makes it evident that they had a decimal system. Oddly enough they used the decimal system for naming only the numbers up to 60. For names of numbers 60 and greater, they used the base sixty. Because of this we still have certain measurements that are based on the number 60, for example, minutes and seconds with respect to both time and measurement of angles.

The Egyptian System

In many ways the numeration system of the Egyptians resembled that of the Babylonians. For example, their numeration system had a base ten. Following are a few Egyptian numerals with their equivalent numerals in our system:

I	(vertical staff) .	.	1
∩	(heel-bone)	.	10
ᓂ	(scroll) .	.	100
𓇬	(lotus flower) .	.	1000
∩∩II	.	. .	22
ᓂ∩II	.	. .	112

The foregoing descriptions are brief and incomplete. For detailed accounts, the reader should consult appropriate texts on the history of mathematics.

Our System of Numeration

We may now define a system of numeration as a system of notation for writing the name of any one of an endless sequence of numbers. Our system of numeration, which is basically of Hindu–Arabic origin, is based on three major principles:

1. The principle of *place value* is the fundamental characteristic of our system of numeration. The principle of place value implies that the meaning or referent of each digit in the numeral is determined by the position it occupies.

Going from right to left, each place is associated with a number ten times as great as the one before. For example, let us consider the numeral 4256. This numeral expresses the number four thousand two hundred fifty-six. The digits in this numeral occupy positions with the following place values:

Thousands	*Hundreds*	*Tens*	*Units*
(1000)	(100)	(10)	(1)
4	2	5	6

2. Our system of numeration is a *base ten* system. (*a*) Only ten symbols are used. These symbols are 0, 1, 2, 3, 4, 5, 6, 7, 8, 9. (*b*) The number associated with the "ones' place" is 10^0,* the "tens' place" is 10^1, the "hundreds' place" is 10^2, and so on. For example, in the numeral 207, the numeral 2 is in the hundreds' place, the numeral 0 is in the tens' place, the numeral 7 is in the ones' place. Thus there are 2 hundreds, 0 tens, and 7 ones.

In our base ten system of numeration we identify places by powers of ten. The following table illustrates this fact:

Place Name	Place Value	Power of Ten
Units	1	10^0
Tens	10	10^1
Hundreds	100	10^2
Thousands	1000	10^3
Ten thousands	10,000	10^4
Hundred thousands	100,000	10^5

Therefore, we can say that

$$4256 = 4(10^3) + 2(10^2) + 5(10^1) + 6(10^0),$$
$$= 4(1000) + 2(100) + 5(10) + 6(1),$$
$$= 4000 + 200 + 50 + 6,$$
$$= \text{four thousand two hundred fifty-six.}$$

3. The third principle is that our system of numeration is *additive*. This fact has already been illustrated. We get the number four thousand two hundred fifty-six from 4256 by adding $4(10^3)$, $2(10^2)$, $5(10^1)$, and $6(10^0)$ as illustrated below:

$$4(10^3) = 4000$$
$$2(10^2) =\ \ 200$$
$$5(10^1) =\ \ \ \ 50$$
$$6(10^0) =\ \ \ \ \ \ 6$$

$$\text{Total} = 4256$$

* Mathematicians say that $n^0 = 1$ by definition for any non-zero n. This definition can be justified in the following manner: in $n^0 = 1$, replace n by the natural number 5. 5^0 should be the same as $\frac{5^2}{5^2} = 5^{2-2}$. But $\frac{5^2}{5^2} = \frac{25}{25} = 1$. Therefore we give meaning to 5^0 by defining it to be 1.

Not all systems exhibit these three properties. For example, all systems of numeration do not use the principle of place value. However, it is this feature that makes our system (Hindu–Arabic) such an excellent system of notation. It permits the writing of numerals for large numbers by the use of only ten symbols. This cannot be done with a nonpositional notation such as the Roman numerals. Some systems of numeration use the additive principle only in part. The Romans for instance, used the additive principle in a numeral like VIII (5 + 3), but they used the subtractive principle in such numerals as IV (5 − 1), and IX (10 − 1).

THE USE OF OTHER BASES IN NUMERATION

Instead of using the base ten in a system of numeration we could use any other number for the base, such as 2, 4, 8, 20, or 60. In fact, some mathematicians believe it would have been preferable to use a base other than ten.

Let us consider a system of numeration using the base two.

1. Here again the chief characteristic of numeration is that of *place value*, that is, the meaning of each digit in a numeral is determined by the position it occupies. For example, the numeral 111 in the base two would be

$$1(2^2) + 1(2^1) + 1(2^0) \text{ (base ten)},$$
$$= 1(4) + 1(2) + 1(1) \text{ (base ten)},$$
$$= 7 \text{ (base ten)}.$$

2. In a *base two* system of numeration, (*a*) two symbols are used, namely, the numerals 1 and 0, and (*b*) the number associated with the first place at the right is 2^0. The number associated with the next place to the left is 2^1, the number associated with the next place to the left is 2^2 and so on. For the base ten we have shown that we identify places by powers of ten; for the base two we identify places by powers of two. Consequently, the numeral in the first place represents the number of ones, the numeral in the second place to the left represents the number of twos, and the third place continuing to the left represents the number of fours, and so on.

3. Naming of numbers is additive for base two as well as for base ten. This principle was illustrated in sub-section 1 above in considering the base two numeral 111. Now let us consider this numeral again using base two only throughout our computations.

Base two   *Base two*

$$111 = 1(10^{10}) + 1(10^1) + 1(10^0),$$
$$= 100 + 10 + 1,$$
$$= 111.$$

In any base, the symbol (10) expresses the number of the base. Consequently in the base two the numeral 10 expresses the number two. That is, the numeral 10 in parentheses represents two. Furthermore, as we needed an exponent of two we represented it also by the numeral 10.

Now let us consider some examples using both bases so that the three principles above will be illustrated. Before doing so, it may be of some assistance to write the numerals for numbers to ten in the base ten and in the base two.

Base Ten	Base Two
1	1
2	10
3	11
4	100
5	101
6	110
7	111
8	1000
9	1001
10	1010

EXAMPLE 1: Reading in the base ten a base ten numeral and a base two numeral.

(a) First let us select the numeral 1111.

Base ten   *Base ten*

$$1111 = 1(10^3) + 1(10^2) + 1(10^1) + (10^0),$$
$$= 1000 + 100 + 10 + 1,$$
$$= \text{one thousand one hundred eleven.}$$

Base two   *Base ten*

$$1111 = 1(2^3) + 1(2^2) + 1(2^1) + 1(2^0),$$
$$= 8 + 4 + 2 + 1,$$
$$= \text{fifteen.}$$

(*b*) Next let us select the numeral 101.

$$\begin{aligned}
\text{Base ten} \quad \text{Base ten} \\
101 = 1(10^2) + 0(10^1) + 1(10^0), \\
= 100 + 1, \\
= \text{one hundred one.}
\end{aligned}$$

$$\begin{aligned}
\text{Base two} \quad \text{Base ten} \\
101 = 1(2^2) + 0(2^1) + 1(2^0), \\
= 4 + 1, \\
= \text{five.}
\end{aligned}$$

EXAMPLE 2: Regrouping objects to illustrate the use of different bases. Let the following symbols represent objects:

# # # # # # # # # # # # # # # # #

Base ten: Here we group by tens.

# # # # # # # # # # # # # # # # #

(10^4)	(10^3)	(10^2)	(10^1)	(10^0)
Ten Thousands	Thousands	Hundreds	Tens	Ones
			1	7

17 (base ten)

Base eight: Here we group by eights.

# # # # # # # # # # # # # # # # #

(8^4)	(8^3)	(8^2)	(8^1)	(8^0)
Four thousand and ninety-sixes	Five hundred and twelves	Sixty-fours	Eights	Ones
			2	1

$$21_8 = 17_{10}$$

Base eight ────── Base ten

Base four: Here we group by fours.

| # # # # | # # # # | # # # # | # # # # | # |

(4^4)	(4^3)	(4^2)	(4^1)	(4^0)
Two hundred and fifty-sixes	Sixty-fours	Sixteens	Fours	Ones
		1	0	1

$$101_4 = 17_{10}$$

Base two: Here we group by twos.

| # # | # # | # # | # # | # # | # # | # # | # # | # |

(2^4)	(2^3)	(2^2)	(2^1)	(2^0)
Sixteens	Eights	Fours	Twos	Ones
1	0	0	0	1

$$10001_2 = 17_{10}*$$

Note that the word names and the symbol names used in the foregoing diagrams are base ten. However, the diagrams used to show groupings can be regarded as diagrams in the particular bases under consideration. One reason for using base ten names in these diagrams is the fact that we do not have names for these groupings in the other bases. Another reason for doing this is that we must learn to relate groupings in other bases to the base ten. This will give greater meaning to the numbers expressed by numerals.

---

* Note that we have made some use of the symbol (=). In the examples above it tells us that we have two different names for the same number.

THE SYSTEM OF NATURAL NUMBERS

In the first section of this chapter we discussed briefly the concept of number. In other words, we gained some feeling for the meaning of number. In this section we return to a more formal study of number, and to a discussion of number systems. Obviously, to write about these ideas, we shall have to use a system of numeration. To do this, we choose our familiar base ten system of numeration.

In our formal study of number and number systems, we shall use the cardinal number approach. That is, the notion of number will be developed through set considerations. For example, the natural numbers will be regarded as properties of sets.

The most familiar and *the simplest numbers are known as the natural numbers.* They form an unending chain of consecutive numbers: 0, 1, 2 . . . 10, 11, 12 . . . 100, 101, 102 . . . .. Any number in this sequence is less than all succeeding numbers. For example, 0 is less than each of the other numbers; 4 is less than 5, and each number that is greater than 5; 11 is less than 12, and each number greater than 12; etc.

The set of natural numbers without zero (0) is known as the set of counting numbers.

OPERATIONS WITH NATURAL NUMBERS

In the second section of this chapter we included a discussion of the properties of a modern system of numeration. Now we shall discuss operations on the set of natural numbers and some of the properties of these operations. An understanding of operations and their properties will enable us to consider the set of natural numbers, together with two operations and their properties, as a number system.

What do we mean by an operation? Let us define it as a *mapping.* This method of definition is general and does not restrict us to define an operation in terms of uses of number. (An understanding of mapping is basic to the study of projective geometry, modern algebra, topology, and most advanced mathematics.)

A mapping is a matching or pairing-off that takes place in the presence of two sets. Each member of one of the sets is paired to a member of the other set. The following diagram illustrates one type of mapping.

$$A = \{a,\ b,\ c\},$$
$$\searrow \downarrow \swarrow$$
$$B = \{1,\ 2,\ 3\}.$$

In such an example, we say that each of a, b, and c is mapped onto 2. We also say that 2 is the image of a, b, and c. But a, b, and c are not images of 2 because the arrows indicate a single direction, A to B. This mapping of A into B is called a *many-to-one* mapping.

Let us consider another kind of situation.

$$A = \{\text{Toronto, Edmonton, Winnipeg}\},$$

$$B = \qquad\qquad \{1,\ 2,\ 3\}.$$

Here the double-headed arrows indicate that Toronto is the image of 1 and 1 is the image of Toronto, Edmonton is the image of 3 and 3 is the image of Edmonton, and Winnipeg is the image of 2 and 2 is the image of Winnipeg. In this example we say that the members of sets A and B are in *one-to-one correspondence*. Thus we observe that a one-to-one correspondence between two sets actually implies *two* one-to-one mappings as each set maps onto the other. In our example, A has been mapped onto B and B has been mapped onto A.

Addition is an example of an operation on the set of natural numbers which we may now explain as a mapping. The operation of addition assigns a definite number called the *sum* to each ordered* pair of natural numbers. For example:

$$(2, 4) \xrightarrow{\ +\ } 2 + 4.$$
$$(3, 1) \xrightarrow{\ +\ } 3 + 1.$$
$$(4, 3) \xrightarrow{\ +\ } 4 + 3.$$

Therefore, we can say that addition is a mapping. It maps the set of ordered pairs of natural numbers onto the set of natural single numbers. ('2 + 4', '3 + 1', and '4 + 3' are names for numbers although two numerals are present in each name. They are names for the numbers 6, 4, and 7, respectively.)

Similarly, we can define the operation of multiplication as a mapping because it assigns a number called the *product* to each ordered pair of numbers. For example:

* An ordered pair is a pair of objects that occur in a special order. This term is more fully defined and illustrated in Chapter 5.

$$(3, 4) \xrightarrow{\times} 3 \times 4.$$
$$(4, 5) \xrightarrow{\times} 4 \times 5.$$
$$(6, 8) \xrightarrow{\times} 6 \times 8.$$

When we write the sentence $15 + 16 = 31$, the equals sign ($=$) tells us that '$15 + 16$' and '31' are names for the same number. '31' is the standard name for this number. Processing is a renaming through computation. One should not confuse processing with the operation. The result of the operation of addition on 15 and 16 is $15 + 16$. The standard name '31' is obtained by processing '$15 + 16$'.

Addition and multiplication are two basic operations in mathematics. Let us now consider some properties of these two operations.

Addition

1. Addition is a *binary* operation. This means that it maps ordered pairs of elements of a set onto elements of the same set. For example, in the operation

$$(4, 5) \xrightarrow{+} 9$$

the pair of numbers (4, 5) maps onto the single number 9. The numbers 4, 5, and 9 are all elements of the set of natural numbers.

2. Addition is a *many-to-one mapping*. This property is illustrated below:

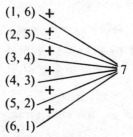

These six ordered pairs map onto the same number.

3. The third property is that addition is *commutative* in the set of natural numbers. In other words, any two natural numbers may be commuted or exchanged without altering the sum. For example:

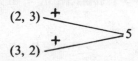

Hence we observe that

$$2 + 3 = 3 + 2, \quad \text{and similarly that}$$
$$4 + 5 = 5 + 4, \quad \text{and}$$
$$6 + 1 = 1 + 6.$$

The generalization of this property is:

For each replacement of m and for each replacement of n,

$$m + n = n + m.$$

The permissible replacements for m and n are the natural numbers. For example:

(*a*) If m is replaced by 60 and n is replaced by 70, then

$$60 + 70 = 70 + 60.$$

(*b*) If m is replaced by 11 and n is replaced by 17, then

$$11 + 17 = 17 + 11.$$

(Variables, equations, etc., will be discussed in another chapter.)

4. The fourth property is that addition is *associative* in the set of natural numbers. The associative property enables us to group three numbers given to us in a definite order in two different ways, so that we may add the numbers two at a time. For example:

$$(3 + 2) + 4 = 3 + (2 + 4).$$
$$4 + (6 + 2) = (4 + 6) + 2.$$
$$(1 + 2) + 3 = 1 + (2 + 3).$$

The generalization of this property is:

For each replacement of m, for each replacement of n, and for each replacement of k,

$$(m + n) + k = m + (n + k).$$

The permissible replacements for m, n, and k are the natural numbers. For example:

(*a*) If m is replaced by 3, n is replaced by 4, and k is replaced by 5, then

$$(3 + 4) + 5 = 3 + (4 + 5).$$
$$7 + 5 = 3 + 9.$$
$$12 = 12.$$

(b) If *m* is replaced by 2, *n* is replaced by 7, and *k* is replaced by 1, then

$$(2 + 7) + 1 = 2 + (7 + 1).$$
$$9 + 1 = 2 + 8.$$
$$10 = 10.$$

We often use both the commutative and associative laws to obtain the desired result. For example, show that $(4 + 3) + 2 = 3 + (2 + 4)$.

$$(4 + 3) + 2 = (3 + 4) + 2, \quad \text{(commutative property)}$$
$$= 3 + (4 + 2), \quad \text{(associative property)}$$
$$= 3 + (2 + 4). \quad \text{(commutative property)}$$

Multiplication

1. Multiplication is also a *binary* operation, since it maps ordered pairs of elements of a set onto single elements of the same set. For example:

$$(4, 5) \xrightarrow{\times} 4 \times 5.$$

By processing '4×5' we get the standard name 20, i.e., $4 \times 5 = 20$.

2. Multiplication is a *many-to-one mapping*. For example:

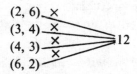

These ordered pairs map onto the same number because '2×6', '3×4', '4×3', and '6×2' are different names for 12.

3. Multiplication is *commutative* in the set of natural numbers. That is to say, any two natural numbers may be commuted or exchanged without altering the product. For example:

$$2 \times 3 = 3 \times 2.$$
$$4 \times 2 = 2 \times 4.$$
$$6 \times 7 = 7 \times 6.$$

The generalization of this property is:

For each replacement of *m* and for each replacement of *n*,

$$mn = nm.$$

The permissible replacements for *m* and *n* are the natural numbers. For example:

If *m* is replaced by 9 and *n* is replaced by 7, then

$$9 \times 7 = 7 \times 9,$$
$$63 = 63.$$

4. Multiplication is *associative* in the set of natural numbers. The associative property enables us to group three numbers given to us in a definite order in two different ways, so that we may multiply the numbers two at a time. For example:

(*a*)
$$2 \times (3 \times 4) = (2 \times 3) \times 4,$$
$$2 \times 12 = 6 \times 4,$$
$$24 = 24.$$

(*b*)
$$(4 \times 2) \times 6 = 4 \times (2 \times 6),$$
$$8 \times 6 = 4 \times 12,$$
$$48 = 48.$$

(*c*)
$$5 \times (2 \times 4) = (5 \times 2) \times 4,$$
$$5 \times 8 = 10 \times 4,$$
$$40 = 40.$$

The generalization of this property is:

For each replacement of *m*, for each replacement of *n*, and for each replacement of *k*,

$$(mn)k = m(nk).$$

The permissible replacements for *m*, *n*, and *k* are the natural numbers. For example:

If *m*, *n*, and *k* are replaced by 4, 5, and 8, respectively, then

$$(4 \times 5)8 = 4(5 \times 8),$$
$$20 \times 8 = 4 \times 40,$$
$$160 = 160.$$

Distributive Law

In the set of natural numbers, *multiplication distributes over addition.* This is known as the *distributive law.*

(*a*)
$$3(2 + 4) = (3 \times 2) + (3 \times 4),$$
$$3 \times 6 = 6 + 12,$$
$$18 = 18.$$

(*b*)
$$4(5 + 6) = (4 \times 5) + (4 \times 6),$$
$$4 \times 11 = 20 + 24,$$
$$44 = 44.$$

The generalization of this property is:

For each replacement of *m*, for each replacement of *n*, and for each replacement of *k*,

$$m(n + k) = mn + mk.$$

The permissible replacements for *m*, *n*, and *k* are the names of the natural numbers.

Using the same numbers as those in example (*a*), let us observe that addition does not distribute over multiplication.

$$3 + (2 \times 4) \neq (3 + 2) \times (3 + 4),$$
$$3 + 8 \neq 5 \times 7,$$
$$11 \neq 35.$$

We have been discussing the set of natural numbers and two operations (addition and multiplication) on this set. We are now in a position to talk about the *system* of natural numbers. Consider the following general definition:

Let S be a set and let addition and multiplication be defined on S. If addition and multiplication are each both commutative and associative and if multiplication distributes over addition, we shall say that S is a number system.

We have seen that the conditions of this definition hold for the natural numbers. Therefore, we can say that, in this sense, the natural numbers together with the operations of addition and multiplication and the properties that we have discussed for these operations constitute a specific number system. Actually, the natural number system is an instance of an abstract number system.

Five Basic Laws or Properties

Five basic properties of the addition and multiplication operations are

the two commutative laws,
the two associative laws,
the distributive law.

These are used extensively in all areas of mathematics, and their significance and meaning will become clearer in the study of other mathematical systems.

Subtraction and Division

In the set of natural numbers the operations of subtraction and division are not commutative. For example, $5 - 2$ is not the same as $2 - 5$. Whereas $5 - 2$ has a meaning, $2 - 5$ is not a natural number. Likewise, $6 \div 3$ is not the same as $3 \div 6$, for $6 \div 3$ has a meaning, but $3 \div 6$ is not a natural number. Therefore, we say that subtraction and division are noncommutative operations in this set of numbers.

Similarly, the operations of subtraction and division are nonassociative in the set of natural numbers. For example, $(8 - 4) - 2$ does not equal $8 - (4 - 2)$, and $(8 \div 4) \div 2$ does not equal $8 \div (4 \div 2)$.

THE PRINCIPLE OF CLOSURE

We say that an operation is closed in a set if the result of the operation on every ordered pair of elements in the set is itself an element in the set. In the set of natural numbers, the binary operations of addition and multiplication are closed because in adding or multiplying two natural numbers, the number we obtain is also a natural number. However, subtraction is not closed in the natural numbers because the number obtained when a natural number is subtracted from another natural number is not always another natural number. Although we can subtract 4 from 8 and get 4, we cannot subtract 8 from 4. In the system of natural numbers, 4 minus 8 is meaningless.

SYSTEM OF INTEGERS

Because subtraction is useful, though not always possible in the system of natural numbers, we shall consider an extension of the system of natural numbers to the *system of integers*. First we must derive a new number for each natural number. With each natural number a, we can associate another number y such that $a + y = 0$. In the condition $a + y = 0$, let us replace a by the natural number 5. In order for $5 + y = 0$ to express a true statement, y must be replaced by -5. Thus $5 + (-5) = 0$. To establish a generalization, we symbolize y by $-a$, and write the sentence

$$a + (-a) = 0.$$

Using this generalization, we are now able to derive the set of negative integers.

The set of integers is made up of three distinct sets of numbers:

1. *The positive integers:* $+1, +2, +3, +4, +5, \ldots$

The counting numbers can now be thought of as the positive integers although they are not identical to them. The set of counting numbers is isomorphic (explained later) to the positive integers.

2. *The integer zero:* (0).

3. *The negative integers:* $\ldots -5, -4, -3, -2, -1$.

On occasion, the first two sets of integers, the positive integers and zero, are considered as a single set and designated as the non-negative integers. In a like manner, the negative integers and zero may be considered as a single set and designated as the non-positive integers.

The integers are also called directed numbers or signed numbers. They are called directed numbers because they may be interpreted geometrically in terms of direction. If we choose a direction to the right for the positive integers, the negative integers take a direction to the left. The origin of these two directions is zero. In mathematics it is customary to choose the direction to the right, or up, as positive and the direction to the left, or down, as negative. In such arrangements it can be seen that zero (the origin) is neither negative nor positive.

The set of integers may be pictured or represented on a number line. This is done by choosing a line, a point, a direction, and a unit distance.

On line x, choose a point P as the origin. We choose to call the direction to the right of P, positive, and the direction to the left of P, negative. Select any point Q such that $Q \neq P$ and Q is to the right of P. The line segment PQ is our unit distance. Now our points

$$\ldots L, M, N, O, P, Q, R, S, T, \ldots$$

are determined by laying off the unit distance so that

$$\ldots = LM = MN = NO = PQ = RS = ST = \ldots$$

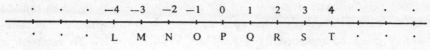

Fig. 20

Now we assign zero (0) to point P; 1 to point Q, -1 to point O; 2 to point R, -2 to point N; 3 to point S, -3 to point M; 4 to point T, -4 to point L; etc. In this way, we set up a correspondence between the set of integers and a subset of the set of points in the line.

OPERATIONS WITH INTEGERS

Let us consider the properties for operations with integers. Our treatment here will be brief, since we have dealt with the operations of natural numbers in some detail.

Addition

1. *For any two integers, there is an integer which is their sum.* For example:

The sum of $(+3)$ and $(+2)$ is $(+3) + (+2)$, or $(+5)$, which is an integer, and the sum of (-3) and $(+2)$ is $(-3) + (+2)$, or -1, which is also an integer.

Other examples are

$$(+7) + (+2) = +9.$$
$$(-5) + (+9) = +4.$$
$$(-3) + (-2) = -5.$$

GENERALIZATION: For each replacement of a, and for each replacement of b,

$$(a, b) \xrightarrow{+} a + b.$$

2. The second property is that addition is *commutative* in the set of integers. For example:

$$(+3) + (+5) = (+5) + (+3).$$
$$(-2) + (+6) = (+6) + (-2).$$
$$(-2) + (-4) = (-4) + (-2).$$

GENERALIZATION: For each replacement of a, and for each replacement of b,

$$a + b = b + a.$$

3. The third property is that addition is *associative* in the system of integers. For example:

$$[(+3) + (+4)] + (+5) = (+3) + [(+4) + (+5)].$$
$$(+6) + [(+4) + (-2)] = [(+6) + (+4)] + (-2).$$
$$[(-2) + (-3)] + (+4) = (-2) + [(-3) + (-4)].$$

GENERALIZATION: For each replacement of a, for each replacement of b, and for each replacement of c,

$$(a + b) + c = a + (b + c).$$

Multiplication

1. *For any two integers, there is an integer which is their product.* For example:

The product of $(+3)$ and $(+4)$ is $(+3) \times (+4)$ or $(+12)$, which is an integer.

GENERALIZATION: For each replacement of a, and for each replacement of b,

$$(a, b) \xrightarrow{\times} a \times b.$$

2. Multiplication is *commutative* in the set of integers. For example:

$$(+3) \times (+6) = (+6) \times (+3).$$
$$(-5) \times (+4) = (+4) \times (-5).$$
$$(+7) \times (+2) = (+2) \times (+7).$$

GENERALIZATION: For each replacement of a, and for each replacement of b,

$$a \times b = b \times a.$$

3. Multiplication is *associative* in the set of integers. For example:

$$(+2)(+3) \times (+4) = (+2) \times (+3)(+4),$$
$$(+6) \times (+4) = (+2) \times (+12),$$
$$+24 = +24.$$

GENERALIZATION: For each replacement of a, for each replacement of b, and for each replacement of c,

$$(ab)c = a(bc).$$

44 ✳

4. Multiplication *distributes over addition* in the set of integers. This is called the distributive law for integers. For example:

$$(+4)[(+5) + (+6)] = (+4)(+5) + (+4)(+6),$$
$$(+4)(+11) = (+20) + (+24),$$
$$+44 = +44.$$

GENERALIZATION: For each replacement of a, for each replacement of b, and for each replacement of c,

$$a(b + c) = ab + ac.$$

We observe that the set of integers, taken together with the operations of addition and multiplication and their properties, satisfies the requirements for a number system. Thus we say that the set of integers forms a number system under the operations of addition and multiplication.

Isomorphism

For purposes of calculation, the non-negative integers are considered to be identical with the natural numbers. But the natural numbers are not really identical with the non-negative integers. They are, in fact, isomorphic to the non-negative integers.

If two number systems, N and N', are isomorphic, (1) there is a one-to-one correspondence between the members or elements of the two systems such that (2), if elements a and b of N correspond to a' and b' of N', then $a + b$ must correspond to $a' + b'$ and ab must correspond to $a'b'$. This permits us to translate from one system to the other to perform the operations. Note that we have said that the natural numbers are isomorphic to the non-negative integers, which are a subset of all the integers. When a set of numbers is isomorphic to a subset of another set of numbers, we say that the second set is an *extension* of the first set. Therefore, we can say that the integers are an extension of the naturals.

Let us give a numerical example of how the operations are preserved under an isomorphism. If N is the set of naturals and N^1 is the set of non-negative integers, we can show one-to-one correspondence between the elements of the two number systems by the following diagram:

N	0	1	2	3	4	5	6	7	8	9 . . .
N^1	0	+1	+2	+3	+4	+5	+6	+7	+8	+9 . . .

Now let us select the elements 2 and 4 of N, and the two corresponding elements $+2$ and $+4$ of N^1. Since $2 + 4 = 6$, and $(+2) + (+4) = +6$, we can say that $2 + 4$ corresponds to $(+2) + (+4)$ because 6 is seen to correspond to $+6$. Furthermore, since $2 \times 4 = 8$ and $(+2) \times (+4) = (+8)$, we can say that 2×4 corresponds to $(+2) \times (+4)$ because 8 is seen to correspond to $+8$.

THE SYSTEM OF RATIONAL NUMBERS

The set of integers extends our power in solving equations because subtraction can be defined on the set of integers. Equations like $x + 4 = 3$ have a solution in the set of integers but not in the set of natural numbers. However, the operation of division is not defined on the set of integers, and therefore we are unable to solve an equation like $3x = 4$. It is obvious that the replacement for x in this equation is 4/3, which is neither a natural number nor an integer.

Because division is not closed in the system of integers, we are led to an extension of the system of integers to the system of *rational numbers*. Following are some examples of rational numbers:

$$\frac{+5}{-3}, \frac{-2}{+3}, \frac{0}{+3}, \frac{+4}{+5}, \frac{+17}{+9} \quad or \quad -\frac{5}{3}, -\frac{2}{3}, 0, \frac{4}{5}, \frac{17}{9}.$$

A rational number is a number that can be expressed in the form a/b where a and b are integers ($b \neq 0$).

For the following reasons $a/0$ is not admitted as a number:

1. Suppose

$$a/0 = x, \quad where \quad a \neq 0.$$

Now the number chosen for x, such that

$$a/0 = x$$

must be such that

$$a = 0 \cdot x.$$

But no matter what number we select for x, this equation cannot be valid since $0 \cdot x = 0$ for any x, and we have assumed that $a \neq 0$. Since we cannot assign any number to $a/0$, we simply do not define it.

2. Next, consider $a/0$ where $a = 0$. Here, a somewhat different problem confronts us:

$$\text{Let} \quad 0/0 = x,$$
$$\text{then} \quad 0 = 0 \cdot x.$$

But this equation yields a true statement for any replacement of x. We avoid the ambiguity by leaving the symbol $0/0$ undefined. However, if $a = 0$, and $b \neq 0$, we have a rational number which is admissible by definition.

$$\text{If} \quad a = 0$$
$$\text{and} \quad b \neq 0,$$
$$\text{let} \quad a/b = x.$$
$$\text{That is} \quad 0/b = x$$
$$\text{and} \quad 0 = x \cdot b.$$
$$\text{Since} \quad b \neq 0, x \text{ must equal } 0,$$
$$\therefore \quad 0/b = 0.$$

We may conclude, therefore, that $0/a$ is zero when a is replaced by any integer other than zero.

Besides zero, we have two major subsets in the set of rationals. They are:

1. The positive rational numbers, such as

$$1/2, \ 3/4, \ 4/1, \ 9/5, \ 41/11, \ 8/1; \quad \text{and}$$

2. The negative rational numbers, such as

$$-4/1, \ -13/4, \ -3/2, \ -2/1, \ -1/2, \ -1/7.$$

In the foregoing subsets, it is seen that most of the numbers are quite unlike any of the integers, for example, $3/4$, $9/5$, $41/11$, $-13/4$, and $-1/7$. These are commonly known as positive or negative fractions, and correspond to points on the number line different from those corresponding to any of the integers. But also in the preceding subsets there are such numbers as $-2/1$, $-4/1$, $4/1$, $8/1$. These four rational numbers correspond to the same points on the number line as the following integers: -2, -4, 2, and 8. This is explained by the fact that the set of integers is isomorphic to a subset of the set of rationals. The set of rationals is, therefore, an extension of the set of integers.

Suppose A and B are arbitrarily chosen elements of a set S, such that $a < b$. The set of numbers, S, is said to be *dense* (or everywhere dense) if, in the interval between a and b, there is a number n such that $a < n < b$. In the set of integers, this definition would not hold, since if $a = 3$ and

$b = 4$, we could not have an integer between 3 and 4. Therefore, we can conclude that the integers do not make up a dense set. In the set of rationals, this definition would apply since between any two rational numbers there is always another rational number. For example, if a and b are two rational numbers, a number n could be $\dfrac{a+b}{2}$.

Let $a = \dfrac{3}{20}$ and $b = \dfrac{7}{30}$.

Then $n = \dfrac{a+b}{2} = \dfrac{\dfrac{3}{20} + \dfrac{7}{30}}{2} = \dfrac{23}{120}$ (another rational number).

Thus we observe that the rational numbers are dense.

The points on a number line that correspond to the rational numbers appear as a solid line, although they do not in fact form a solid line. Let us see how we can set up a correspondence between some of the rational numbers and a subset of the set of points in a line. We first choose a line, a point, a direction, and a unit distance.

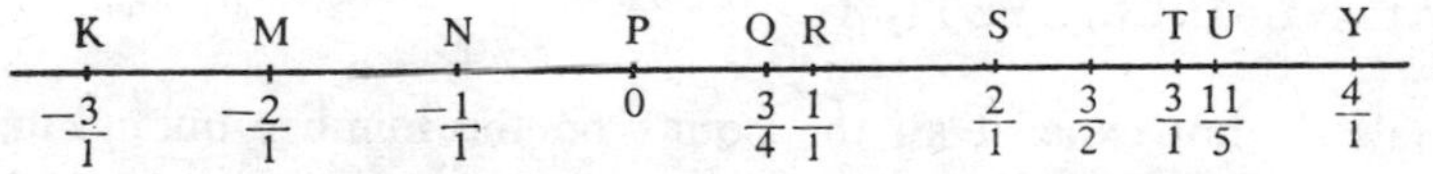

Fig. 21

On line x, choose a point P as origin. Again we shall choose to call the direction to the right of P, positive, and the direction to the left of P, negative. Next select a point R to the right of P so that $R \neq P$. The line segment PR is our unit distance. The number zero (0) is assigned to the origin P, and the number $1/1$, or 1, is assigned to the point R. The number $-1/1$, or -1, is assigned to the point N, which is one unit distance to the left of P. The number $2/1$ is assigned to the point T, which is two unit distances to the right of P. The number $-2/1$ is assigned to the point M, which is two unit distances to the left of P. To assign the number $3/4$ to a point on the line, we divide the unit distance into four equal parts and lay off three of these equal parts from P and to the right. Thus $3/4$ is assigned to Q. To assign the number $11/5$ to a point on the line, we divide the unit distance into five equal parts and lay off eleven of these equal parts from P and to the right. Thus $11/5$ is assigned to U. Similarly, other rational numbers may be assigned to points on line x.

To generalize, we can assign a point on the line to a rational number $\frac{h}{k}$ ($k \neq 0$) by dividing the unit distance into k equal parts and laying off h of these equal parts, to the right of the origin (0) if $h > 0$, and to the left if $h < 0$.

Properties of Operations with Rational Numbers

As in the system of natural numbers and the system of integers, the operations of addition and multiplication of rational numbers obey the commutative, associative, and distributive laws. Consequently, we can say that the rational numbers also constitute a number system under addition and multiplication.

Since the description of the basic operations of addition and multiplication have been given in earlier sections of this chapter, it is assumed that such a detailed treatment need not be repeated for the set of rational numbers.

THE REAL NUMBER SYSTEM

The rationals do not exhaust all the points on the number line. For example, the number $\sqrt{2}$, which is not a rational number, can be assigned to a point on a number line.

We can locate the point corresponding to $\sqrt{2}$ on a number line in the following manner:

On line x select a point P as origin. Select a point B on the line and to the right of P such that $PB = 1$ (unit distance). At B erect a perpendicular, and mark on it the point A, such that $AB = PB = 1$. Join PA. With center P and radius PA describe an arc cutting line x at Q. Then $PA = PQ$.

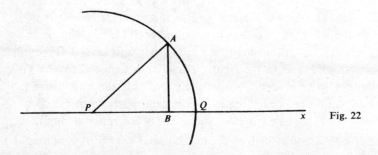

Fig. 22

By the theorem of Pythagoras:

$$PA^2 = PB^2 + AB^2,$$
$$= (1)^2 + (1)^2,$$
$$= 1 + 1,$$
$$= 2.$$
$$PA^2 = 2,$$
$$PA = \sqrt{2},$$
$$\therefore \quad PQ = \sqrt{2}.$$

Thus $\sqrt{2}$ is assigned to point Q.

It can be shown that there is no rational number whose square is 2.

THEOREM: The square root of 2 is not a rational number.

PROOF: Assume $\sqrt{2}$ is rational.

Let x denote a positive rational such that

$$x^2 = 2.$$

Any rational number can be expressed in the form of $a/b(b \neq 0)$. Any such fraction a/b can be reduced to a lowest term form so that $x = m/n$. The positive integers m and n must now be prime to each other, that is, they will have only 1 as their common factor.

$$\text{If} \quad x^2 = 2,$$

then $\dfrac{m^2}{n^2} = 2$ and $m^2 = 2n^2$. If this is true, m^2 must be even and, therefore, m must be even. Since m is even, we have $m = 2d$ (d a positive integer) and since $m^2 = 2n^2$, then

$$2n^2 = (2d)^2,$$
$$= 4d^2,$$
$$n^2 = 2d^2.$$

Therefore, n^2 is even and n is even. We have proved that both m and n are even and hence not prime to each other. This is contrary to our earlier supposition that m and n were prime to each other and therefore not both even. Because of this contradiction we must reject the assumption that x is a rational number in the original equation $x^2 = 2$, and therefore conclude that the $\sqrt{2}$ is not a rational number.

Numbers such as $\sqrt{2}$ and $\sqrt{5}$ which are not rational are called *irrational*.

All rational and irrational numbers can be expressed as decimals. A study of such decimals will indicate that every rational number can be expressed as a non-terminating repeating decimal. For example:

$$3/4 = .75000 \text{ (the zeros repeat)}, \quad \text{and}$$
$$1/3 = .333\ldots.$$

The irrational numbers can be expressed as non-terminating and non-repeating decimals. For example:

$$\sqrt{2} = 1.414213562\ldots.$$

The real number system is defined to include all rational and irrational numbers. It completely fills out the number line. The reals are called decimal numbers since each can be expressed by a decimal. To represent the real numbers between −2 and 4, and including −2 and 4, on a number line, we draw a continuous line segment between and including these two points. The line segment includes all the points between −2 and 4 and also the points −2 and 4. In this manner each real number under consideration has been assigned to a point on the number line.

Following is a graph of the set of real numbers between and including −2 and 4.

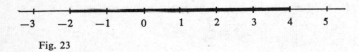

Fig. 23

The four number systems described in this chapter are those that are basic to the mathematics program from Grades 1 to 12 inclusive. We could proceed to the study of complex numbers but this is not necessary for our purpose here. If and when any special numbers beyond the reals are needed, their introduction would not be difficult following a good basic program that includes the number systems from the naturals to the reals.

SUBTRACTION AND DIVISION AS INVERSES OF ADDITION AND MULTIPLICATION

Subtraction may be defined as the inverse of addition, and division may be defined as the inverse of multiplication. This is one reason for regarding addition and multiplication as the principal operations in arithmetic and algebra.

The meaning of *inverse* in mathematics is similar to its meaning in common everyday experiences. We can think of it as an *undoing* operation. Many things we do each day, we necessarily undo. For example, we go shopping and we return home. The lights we switch on we eventually switch off. We go to bed at night and get up in the morning. In arithmetic we add 4 to 2 and get 6. In order to get back to 2, we take 4 from 6. This is an inverse operation. Similarly, if we multiply 2 by 4, we get 8, and to get back to 2, we divide 8 by 4. Obviously, this also is an inverse operation.

If we multiply a quantity by 3, the inverse operation of division by 3 would bring us back to the original quantity. To perform this inverse operation, we divide by 3 or multiply by 1/3, for example:

$$\text{If } 3x = 9/4,$$
$$\text{then } 3x \times 1/3 = 9/4 \times 1/3,$$
$$\text{and } x = 3/4.$$

ADDITIVE AND MULTIPLICATIVE
IDENTITIES AND INVERSES

In this chapter, we have discussed the major laws for addition and multiplication, such as the commutative, associative, and distributive laws. We shall now observe some other properties of the operations that are useful in algebra. These additional properties are not required for a number system but are necessary in constructing other kinds of mathematical systems, which we shall discuss in a later chapter.

1. Zero (0) is called the *identity element for addition* because zero (0) added to any number a gives that same number. For example:

$$4 + 0 = 4.$$
$$7 + 0 = 7.$$

That is,

$a + 0 = a$ (Identity element property for the real numbers under addition).

2. We call $-a$ the *inverse element for addition* (or the additive inverse of a) because, for each replacement of a from the set of real numbers, $-a$ is a number which on addition to a gives zero (0). For example:

$$4 + (-4) = 0.$$
$$7 + (-7) = 0.$$

That is,

$a + (-a) = 0$ (Inverse element property for the real numbers under addition).

3. 1 is called the *identity element for multiplication* because, when 1 is multiplied by any number a, it yields that same number. For example:

$$3 \times 1 = 3.$$
$$5 \times 1 = 5.$$

That is,

$a \times 1 = a$ (Identity element property for the real numbers under multiplication).

4. We call $\dfrac{1}{a}$ the *inverse element for multiplication* (or the multiplicative inverse of a) because, for each replacement of a, $a \neq 0$, from the set of real numbers, $\dfrac{1}{a}$ is a number which on multiplication by a gives 1. For example:

$$3 \times 1/3 = 1.$$
$$5 \times 1/5 = 1.$$

That is,

$a \times \dfrac{1}{a} = 1 (a \neq 0)$ (Inverse element property for the real numbers under multiplication).

Note that zero (0) has no multiplicative inverse, since the symbol 1/0 is an undefined symbol.

SOME APPLICATIONS OF ALGEBRAIC LAWS

Some may wonder about the utility of these properties or laws. However, with increased understanding and use of these laws, it should be evident that elementary problems in algebra can be solved and proofs of theorems can be made mathematically without reliance on "rules of thumb". The following examples are included to illustrate this fact:

1. TO PROVE:

$$2x + 3x = 5x.$$

PROOF:

$2x + 3x = x \cdot 2 + x \cdot 3,$ (commutative law for multiplication)
$x2 + x3 = x(2 + 3),$ (distributive law)
$x(2 + 3) = x \cdot 5,$ (processing '2 + 3')
$x \cdot 5 \quad = 5x,$ (commutative law for multiplication)
Hence $2x + 3x = 5x.$

2. TO PROVE:
$$(x + 3)(x + 2) = x^2 + 5x + 6.$$

PROOF:

$$
\begin{aligned}
(x + 3)(x + 2) &= (x + 3)x + (x + 3)2, &\text{(distributive law)}\\
&= x(x + 3) + 2(x + 3), &\text{(commutative law)}\\
&= x^2 + 3x + 2x + 6, &\text{(distributive law)}\\
&= x^2 + x3 + x2 + 6, &\text{(commutative law)}\\
&= x^2 + x(3 + 2) + 6, &\text{(distributive law)}\\
&= x^2 + x5 + 6; &\text{(distributive law)}\\
&= x^2 + 5x + 6. &\text{(commutative law)}
\end{aligned}
$$

PROBLEMS FOR REVIEW

1. Outline the chief differences between our system of numeration and that of the early Romans.

2. For each of the following numerals (base ten), write Babylonian and Roman numerals that express the same number:
   (*a*) 32, (*b*) 81, (*c*) 103.

3. Change the numeral 65 (base ten) to a numeral that expresses the same number in:
   (*a*) base eight, (*b*) base two, (*c*) base four, (*d*) base nine.

4. Construct a multiplication table in the base three.

5. By means of diagrams, illustrate:
   (*a*) one-to-one correspondence,
   (*b*) many-to-one mapping.

6. If x and y are replaced by integers, which of the following expressions will always represent integers:
   (*a*) $x - y$, (*b*) $x \cdot y$, (*c*) $x \div y$.

7. Use the commutative and associative laws to prove
   (*a*) $(3 + 4) + 7 = 4 + (7 + 3)$,
   (*b*) $(x + y) + z = (z + x) + y$.

8. Prove that subtraction is *not* associative.

9. Show that the inverse element property for multiplication does not hold for the set of integers.

10. Real numbers may be defined as "the set of all decimals". Explain.

BIBLIOGRAPHY

1. ADLER, IRVING. *The New Mathematics*. New York: The John Day Company, 1958.

2. ALLENDOERFER, C. B. and OAKLEY, C. O. *Principles of Mathematics*. New York: McGraw-Hill Company, 1955.

3. DUBISCH, RAY. *The Nature of Number*. New York: The Ronald Press Company, 1952.

4. *Insights into Modern Mathematics*. 23rd Yearbook: The National Council of Teachers of Mathematics, 1957.

5. NIVEN, IVAN. *Irrational Numbers*. John Wiley and Sons Inc. The Mathematical Association of America, 1956.

6. RICHARDSON, M. *Fundamentals of Mathematics*. New York: The Macmillan Company, 1958.

4 CONDITIONS IN ONE VARIABLE

SENTENCES

To communicate ideas in writing or in speech we use sentences.

> The flowers are in bloom.
> The barn is painted red.
> Mary is in Grade XII.

Such sentences are usually known as declarative sentences. A declarative sentence expresses an idea about which a decision can be made as to whether the idea is true or false but not both. Declarative sentences that express true or false ideas are called *closed* sentences. The ideas that are expressed by closed sentences are called *statements*. Observe, then, that a statement is true or false but not both. A closed sentence is a symbol that expresses a statement. As such, it is the name of a statement. The foregoing examples may be called non-mathematical closed sentences.

Sentences that are not closed are known as *open* sentences. Whereas *closed sentences express statements*, *open sentences express conditions* that, when satisfied, produce true statements. This is a non-mathematical open sentence: "——— invented the telephone". It is not appropriate to say that this sentence expresses a statement that is true or false. If we make a proper replacement for the blank (———), the sentence expresses a true statement. It becomes a false statement if any other replacement is made. This open sentence expresses a true statement if the blank is replaced by the name Alexander Graham Bell.

It is also necessary to use sentences in mathematical discourse. For example, the sentence $2 + 3 = 5$ is a mathematical sentence that expresses the same thought as does the verbal sentence: Two plus three equals five. Other examples of mathematical sentences are:

$$7 + 9 = 16.$$
$$x + 2 = 7.$$
$$x + y = 6.$$

EQUATIONS

We shall choose to define an equation as a true statement that is expressed by a sentence containing the symbol for "equals". The following sentences express equations: $4 + 2 = 6$, $9 = 4 + 5$, and $3 \times 7 = 21$. Observe that the condition $x + 3 = 7$ is not an equation, since it is not a statement that is true. However, note that the condition $x + 3 = 7$ is expressed by an open sentence that has the symbol for "equals". For this reason, we often refer to the condition $x + 3 = 7$ as an equation. When we do this, we really mean that it is a condition for an equation. This implies that it is our intention to obtain an equation from the condition $x + 3 = 7$ after we make replacements.

Now let us consider some statements and conditions involving natural numbers:

$$(K) \quad 3 + 4 = 7.$$
$$(L) \quad 5 + 4 = 8.$$
$$(M) \quad x + 2 = 7.$$
$$(N) \quad y - 3 = 5.$$

Observe that sentence K expresses a statement that is true, and that sentence L expresses a statement that is false. Therefore, K and L are closed sentences. Sentences M and N are open sentences since they express conditions or requirements about numbers.

When used in closed sentences, the symbol for "equals" ($=$) means that we have two different names for the same object or number. For example, in the sentence $3 + 4 = 7$, the symbol $3 + 4$ and the symbol 7 are names for the same number. In the sentence $x + 2 = 7$, the "equals" sign implies that we intend to find a replacement for x, such that the symbol $x + 2$ becomes a name for 7.

INEQUALITIES

The following mathematical sentences are somewhat different from the ones we have been discussing:

$$(P) \quad 8 > 6.$$
$$(Q) \quad 2 + 3 < 4.$$
$$(R) \quad x > 3.$$
$$(S) \quad y - 4 < 8.$$

The symbol $>$ is read "is greater than" and the symbol $<$ is read "is less than". Because of the presence of these symbols of inequality, all of these sentences express *inequalities*. The statement expressed by P is true because 8 is greater than 6. The statement expressed by Q is false because $2 + 3$, or 5, is not less than 4. We have observed that sentences that express statements that are either true or false are called closed sentences. Therefore, sentences P and Q are closed sentences.

Sentence R expresses a condition. The condition will yield a true statement if x is replaced by 4 or some number greater than 4, but it will yield a false statement if x is replaced by 1, 2, or 3. Sentence S also expresses a condition. The condition will yield a true statement if y is replaced by 11 or a number less than 11, but will yield a false statement if y is replaced by 12 or a number greater than 12.

Sentences R and S are open sentences since they express conditions. Conditions, you recall, do not have truth value.

PLACEHOLDER

In our conversation or writing we often wish to consider a large number of sentences that are similar in form. Let us examine a group of such non-mathematical sentences:

> Mr. Smith is a soldier.
> Mr. Jones is a soldier.
> Mr. James is a soldier.
> Mr. White is a soldier.
> Mr. Black is a soldier.

Note that these sentences have a basic form or pattern, because only one word or term (the name) is different in each. The basic pattern for these sentences is "——— is a soldier" or "x is a soldier". But this is an open sentence because, as it stands, it is neither true nor false. It will be true of certain names, but it will be false of others. The symbol x holds the place for the name of a soldier and is known as a placeholder. When the name of a person who is a soldier is substituted for x, *the sentence then expresses a true statement*.

Now let us consider a number of mathematical sentences:

$$1 + 3 = 7.$$
$$2 + 3 = 7.$$
$$3 + 3 = 7.$$
$$4 + 3 = 7.$$
$$5 + 3 = 7.$$
$$6 + 3 = 7.$$

Again we have a number of sentences that display a common pattern, since only the first numeral is different in each sentence. The open sentence $x + 3 = 7$ is a concise method of describing this long list of sentences.

We define a placeholder as a symbol that is replaceable by names of objects or numbers. The symbol for a placeholder is usually a small letter of the alphabet; such as x, y, a, or b. It could be indicated by other symbols such as a blank (—), or a box ($\square$), or a question mark (?). For example:

——— is a member of the football team.

$$4 + \square = 8.$$
$$3 + 4 = ?$$

CONDITION: VARIABLE: UNIVERSE

We have said that an open sentence expresses a condition. A condition, you recall, is a requirement made by an open sentence; $x + 3 = 7$ and $2x < 9$ are examples of conditions.

Since a condition is an idea expressed by an open sentence, it cannot have a placeholder. Open sentences have placeholders. Conditions have variables that we mentally replace with numbers. Numerals are replacements for placeholders. Numbers are replacements for variables.

If, for example, we replace the variable x by the number 4 in the condition $x + 3 = 7$, we obtain a true statement. Notice that we obtain statements from conditions after we have replaced the variable.

Observe that we have been talking about replacing the variable in a condition by numbers. The question now arises as to what numbers we can use as replacements for the variable. The numbers we can use are called permissible replacements and, taken together, they form a set that is called the universe of discourse for the variable. The universe for a variable, then, is the set whose members may replace the variable. Usually, the universe of discourse is decided upon in advance, or is obtained as the result of some problem situation.

THE NAME-REFERENT DISTINCTION

The study of mathematics should help us to be more precise in our thinking and in our language. If we speak of names of objects as though we were speaking of the objects themselves, we cannot help but sacrifice precision in thought and language. This is one of the reasons we have for choosing to make a distinction between the names of objects or ideas and their referents, which are the actual objects or ideas. It may be helpful at this point to summarize the name-referent distinctions we have encountered thus far. They are as follows:

Name (*symbol*)	Referent (*object or idea*)
numeral	number
closed sentence	statement
open sentence	condition
placeholder	variable

Since traditionally we have not always made such distinctions, we may require a little practice before we can always do so. In the remainder of this book we shall distinguish between names and their referents in order to strengthen our precision in thought and language.

SOLUTION SETS

We have said that when the variable in a condition is replaced by a member of the universe, a statement is obtained from the condition. The statement may be either true or false but not both. The members of the universe that convert the condition into a true statement form a subset of the universe. This subset of the universe is known as the *solution set* of the condition. Solution set is defined as *the set whose members make true statements from a condition upon replacement for the variable.* The solution set of a condition may be the universe itself, or a proper subset of the universe. This implies that a solution set may be the null set, since a null set is a proper subset of any set except itself.

In traditional mathematics, we often talk about the "answers" or "solutions" of problems. An answer or a solution to a problem is simply a member of the solution set. Note that since the solution set is always a subset of the universe, we must identify the universe before finding the solution set.

For the condition $x + 3 = 7$ the solution set is the subset of the universe that satisfies the condition. This set can be symbolized as follows:

$$\{x \mid x + 3 = 7\},$$

which is read "the set of all x, satisfying the condition that $x + 3 = 7$". If the universe is $\{1, 2, 3, 4, 5\}$, there are five possible replacements for the variable in $x + 3 = 7$. However, only one member, 4, would convert the condition into a true statement. Therefore, we say that $\{4\}$ is the solution set of the condition $x + 3 = 7$.

In the same universe, $\{1, 2, 3, 4, 5\}$, let us consider the two conditions expressed below:

1. $x + 3 < 7$.
2. $x + 3 > 9$.

The solution set of $x + 3 < 7$ is $\{1, 2, 3\}$. In such an example each member of the solution set is a solution of $x + 3 < 7$. Now let us consider the condition $x + 3 > 9$. Since no members of our universe satisfy this condition, its solution set is empty or is the null set (ϕ).

SOLUTION SETS OF CONDITIONS IN ONE VARIABLE

In determining the solution sets for the following conditions, let us decide (1) to use set terminology and notation, and (2) to graph the solution sets whenever convenient.

You will recall that the solution set of $x + 3 = 7$ is $\{4\}$. Now we can use the number line to graph this solution set. We shall do this by drawing a small circle around the dot for the point corresponding to the member of the solution set. Remember that $U = \{1, 2, 3, 4, 5\}$.

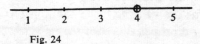

Fig. 24

Observe that a condition, such as $x + 3 = 7$, selects from the universe just those things of which it is true.

Now let us consider other conditions. First, we shall determine their solution sets, and then, by means of number lines, we shall graph their solution sets. For each of the first seven examples, the universe is $\{1, 2, 3, 4, 5, 6, 7, 8, 8, 10\}$.

1. $x - 3 = 3$.

   (*a*) The solution set is $\{x \mid x - 3 = 3\}$ or $\{6\}$.

   (*b*) The graph of this solution set is shown in Figure 25.

Fig. 25

2. $x + 2 = 7$.

   (*a*) The solution set is $\{x \mid x + 2 = 7\}$ or $\{5\}$.

   (*b*) The graph of this solution set is shown in Figure 26.

Fig. 26

3. $\dfrac{x + 4}{2} = 6$.

   (*a*) The solution set is $\left\{x \mid \dfrac{x + 4}{2} = 6\right\}$ or $\{8\}$.

   (*b*) The graph of this solution set is shown in Figure 27.

Fig. 27

4. $\dfrac{x - 3}{3} = 2$.

   (*a*) The solution set is $\left\{x \mid \dfrac{x - 3}{3} = 2\right\}$ or $\{9\}$.

   (*b*) The graph of this solution set is shown in Figure 28.

Fig. 28

We have been considering conditions for equations. In the next three examples, we shall consider conditions for inequalities.

5. $x > 8$.

    (a) The solution set is $\{x \mid x > 8\}$ or $\{9, 10\}$.

    (b) The graph of this solution set is shown in Figure 29.

Fig. 29

6. $x + 2 < 6$.

    (a) The solution set is $\{x \mid x + 2 < 6\}$ or $\{1, 2, 3\}$.

    (b) The graph of this solution set is shown in Figure 30.

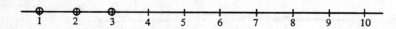

Fig. 30

7. $x - 2 > 4$.

    (a) The solution set is $\{x \mid x - 2 > 4\}$ or $\{7, 8, 9, 10\}$.

    (b) The graph of this solution set is shown in Figure 31.

Fig. 31

Now let us use a different universe for each of the final three examples of conditions. This will help to establish the importance of the universe in determining solution sets.

8. $2x + 1 = 6$.

    $U = $ the set of rational numbers.

    (a) The solution set is $\{x \mid 2x + 1 = 6\}$ or $\{2\frac{1}{2}\}$.

    (b) The graph of this solution set is shown in Figure 32.

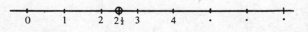

Fig. 32

If the universe is the set of integers, then the solution set of $2x + 1 = 6$ is the null or empty set.

9. $2x > 4$.

    $U =$ the set of real numbers.

    (*a*) The solution set is $\{x \mid 2x > 4\}$ or $\{x \mid x > 2\}$.

    (*b*) The graph of this solution set is shown in Figure 33.

Fig. 33

The sign [)], placed next to a numeral on a number line, indicates that the solution set does not include the number referent of the numeral. If the line is drawn up to a numeral without such a sign, we shall agree that the number represented by the numeral is included.

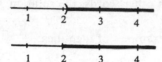 2 is not included in solution set.

2 is included in solution set.

Fig. 34

10. $x < -2$.

    $U =$ the set of real numbers.

    (*a*) The solution set is $\{x \mid x < -2\}$.

    (*b*) The graph of this solution is shown in Figure 35.

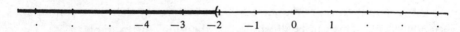

Fig. 35

Here are two interesting and important generalizations with respect to solution sets of certain conditions:

1. *The solution sets for any three conditions such as* $x = a$, $x > a$, *and* $x < a$ *will fill out the complete number line in the universe of real numbers.*

    If we let $a = 2$, our conditions will be $x = 2$, $x > 2$, and $x < 2$.

    The solution set for $x = 2$ is $\{x \mid x = 2\}$.

    The solution set for $x > 2$ is $\{x \mid x > 2\}$.

    The solution set for $x < 2$ is $\{x \mid x < 2\}$.

The graph of these three solution sets is shown in Figure 36.

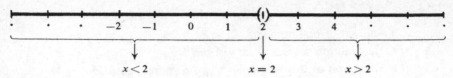

Fig. 36

2. *The solution set of an identity is the entire universe.*

Let us consider the condition $x + 1 = 1 + x$, in the universe of real numbers. The solution set will be $\{x \mid x + 1 = 1 + x\}$ or U. The graph is the complete line.

The condition $x + 1 = 1 + x$ is a special type of condition known as an *identity*. *An identity is a condition from which true statements are formed for each replacement of the variable.* In other words, the solution set for any identity is the entire universe.

The conditions expressed below are other examples of identities:

$$x + 2x = 3x.$$
$$x^2 - 4 = (x + 2)(x - 2).$$

EQUIVALENT CONDITIONS

If two conditions have the same solution set, we say that these conditions are equivalent. This can be illustrated by the following example:

$$12x - 7 = -31.$$
$$x + 4 = 2.$$

If the universe is the set of real numbers, the solution set of $12x - 7 = -31$ is $\{x \mid 12x - 7 = -31\}$ or $\{-2\}$.

The solution set of $x + 4 = 2$ is $\{x \mid x + 4 = 2\}$ or $\{-2\}$.

Since these two conditions have the same solution set, we say that they are equivalent conditions. The two conditions are obviously different but they are equivalent, since they have the same solution set. It is important to note that we define equivalent conditions in terms of their solution sets.

Let us consider two other conditions:

$$2x < 8.$$
$$3x - 5 < 7.$$

In the universe of natural numbers, the solution set of $2x < 8$ is $\{1, 2, 3\}$ and the solution set of $3x - 5 < 7$ is also $\{1, 2, 3\}$. Thus $2x < 8$ and $3x - 5 < 7$ are equivalent conditions in this universe.

COMPOUND STATEMENTS AND
COMPOUND CONDITIONS

Two simple statements can be combined to form a compound statement. For example:

1. John is a policeman.
2. John is Irish.

These two simple statements may be combined into the compound statement, "John is a policeman, and John is Irish".

Let us make another compound statement from two other simple statements:

1. Tom is a track star.
2. Tom is a football player.

From these two simple statements we can make the compound statement, "Tom is a track star, or Tom is a football player".

Observe that connectives *and* and *or* are used above to connect two simple statements to form a compound statement. Here also we are interested in knowing whether a statement is true or false. The first compound statement (or any compound statement using the connective *and*) is true just in case both parts are true. On the other hand, the second compound statement (or any compound statement using the connective *or*) is true just in case at least one of the parts is true. In the first sentence, if John is, in fact, a policeman but is not Irish, the compound statement is false. In the second sentence, if Tom is, in fact, a track star but is not a football player, the compound statement is true. The connectives *and* and *or* are, then, different in their effects.

Now let us consider the compound mathematical statements expressed below:

1. $4 + 5 = 9$ *and* $6 - 5 = 2$.
2. $4 + 5 = 9$ *or* $6 - 5 = 1$.

The first compound statement is false since $6 - 5 = 2$ is a false statement. The second compound statement is true since at least one of the parts is true. In this case it happens that both $4 + 5 = 9$ and $6 - 5 = 1$ are true statements.

We have been discussing compound mathematical statements. They are called statements since they are either true or false. Now let us consider compound conditions. Such conditions are made up of two or more simple conditions. For example, from the two simple conditions, $x + 3 = 6$ and $x < 4$, we can make the compound conditions expressed below using the connectives *and* and *or*:

1. $x + 3 = 6$ *and* $x < 4$.
2. $x + 3 = 6$ *or* $x < 4$.

We must now learn how to determine the solution sets of compound conditions. The first thing we must know is the universe. In finding the solution sets for the conditions expressed above, we shall let $U = \{1, 2, 3, 4, 5, 6\}$.

First, let us consider the compound condition $x + 3 = 6$ *and* $x < 4$. You will recall that the solution set is the set whose members, upon replacement for the variable, form true statements from the condition. We have learned that in order for a compound statement that contains the connective *and* to be true, both simple statements must be true.

The solution set of. $x + 3 = 6$ is $\{3\}$, and the solution set of $x < 4$ is $\{1, 2, 3\}$. Remember that the universe is $\{1, 2, 3, 4, 5, 6\}$. We wish to find the members of the universe that will satisfy both of the simple conditions. In other words, we want to find just those members of the universe that will make true statements from both of the simple conditions. It is evident that the solution set of the compound condition is $\{3\}$, since 3 is the only member of the universe that satisfies both simple conditions.

We can picture the solution set for this compound condition as follows:

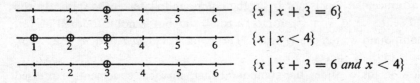

Fig. 37

The solution set of a compound condition that involves the connective *and* will be just those members of the universe that belong to the solution sets of both simple conditions of the compound condition. You will recall that this is our definition of the intersection of two sets.

Now let us determine and graph the solution set of this compound condition through our knowledge of intersection.

Let A = the solution set of $x + 3 = 6$, and
B = the solution set of $x < 4$.

Then the solution set of the compound condition is just those members of the universe that belong to both A and B. By definition this solution set is $A \cap B$. Therefore, if

$$U = \{1, 2, 3, 4, 5, 6\},$$
$$A = \{x \mid x + 3 = 6\} = \{3\}, \quad \text{and}$$
$$B = \{x \mid x < 4\} = \{1, 2, 3\},$$
$$\text{then } A \cap B = \{3\}.$$

With more experience in determining the solution sets of compound conditions that involve the connective *and*, we shall note that knowledge of intersection is of definite assistance.

From the foregoing, it should be clear that the solution set of the compound condition, $x + 3 = 6$ *and* $x < 4$, is $\{x \mid x + 3 = 6 \text{ and } x < 4\}$ or $\{x \mid x + 3 = 6\} \cap \{x \mid x < 4\}$.

GENERALIZATION: On occasion it is convenient and useful to denote a sentence by a symbol like P or Q. If the sentence is one in which x is a placeholder we can call the sentence P_x. If we have a sentence in which y is a placeholder we can call the sentence Q_y. For example:

$$P_x: x + 3 = 7,$$
$$Q_y: y - 3 = 6.$$

Using this notation, the general form of a sentence using the connective *and*, and expressing a compound condition, is P_x and Q_y.

$$\{x \mid P_x \text{ and } Q_y\} = \{x \mid P_x\} \cap \{x \mid Q_y\}.$$

This can be clarified by means of a Venn diagram as shown in Figure 38.

Now let us consider the compound condition

$$x + 3 = 6 \text{ or } x < 4.$$
$$U = \{1, 2, 3, 4, 5, 6\}.$$

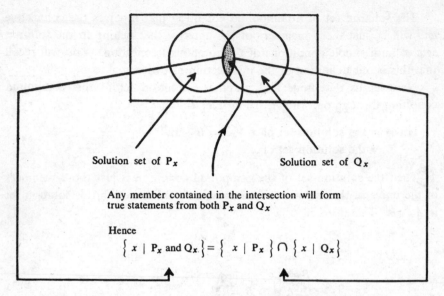

Solution set of P_x Solution set of Q_x

Any member contained in the intersection will form
true statements from both P_x and Q_x

Hence

$$\left\{ x \mid P_x \text{ and } Q_x \right\} = \left\{ x \mid P_x \right\} \cap \left\{ x \mid Q_x \right\}$$

Fig. 38

To find the solution set for this compound condition, we must find the
replacements for x from the universe that form true statements from at least
one of the simple conditions. We must do this because we have learned that
a compound statement involving the connective *or* is true just in case at
least one of its simple statements is true. The solution set of $x + 3 = 6$ is
{3}, and the solution set of $x < 4$ is {1, 2, 3}. Therefore, the solution set of
the compound condition is {1, 2, 3}. If the variable x is replaced by 3, true
statements are formed from both parts of the compound condition. If we
replace the variable x by 1 or 2, false statements are obtained from the first
part but the second part yields true statements. Because only one simple
statement needs to be true to make the compound statement true, it is
evident that the solution set of $x + 3 = 6$ *or* $x < 4$ is {1, 2, 3}.

Let us illustrate the solution set of this compound condition by graphs.

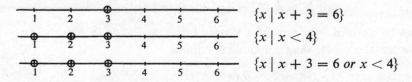

$\{x \mid x + 3 = 6\}$

$\{x \mid x < 4\}$

$\{x \mid x + 3 = 6 \text{ } or \text{ } x < 4\}$

Fig. 39

Observe that this is an example of the *union* of two sets. The solution set of the foregoing compound condition is made up of just those members of the universe that belong to the solution sets of either $x + 3 = 6$ or $x < 4$ or of both. This is identical to the definition of union given on page 17.

Let us look at this same problem again as the union of two sets. Thus, if

$$U = \{1, 2, 3, 4, 5, 6\},$$
$$A = \{3\}, \text{ the solution set of } x + 3 = 6, \text{ and}$$
$$B = \{1, 2, 3\}, \text{ the solution set of } x < 4,$$
$$\text{then } A \cup B = \{1, 2, 3\}.$$

We may conclude, therefore, that the solution set of $x + 3 = 6$ *or* $x < 4$ is $\{x \mid x + 3 = 6 \text{ or } x < 4\}$ or $\{x \mid x + 3 = 6\} \cup \{x \mid x < 4\}$.

The solution set of such a compound condition is shown by the Venn diagram in Figure 40.

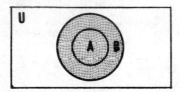

Fig. 40

GENERALIZATION: The general form of a sentence using the connective *or* and expressing a compound condition is P_x or Q_x.

$$\{x \mid P_x \text{ or } Q_x\} = \{x \mid P_x\} \cup \{x \mid Q_x\}.$$

In summary, then, we can regard the solution set of any compound condition with the connective "and" as an intersection of two solution sets, and the solution set of any compound condition with the connective "or" as the union of two sets. We shall see that this fact is very useful to us in later work.

Our generalizations are as follows: If the symbols P_x and Q_x express conditions, the solution sets of the compound conditions

1. P_x *and* Q_x, and
2. P_x *or* Q_x

will be

1. $\{x \mid P_x \text{ and } Q_x\}$ or $\{x \mid P_x\} \cap \{x \mid Q_x\}$, and
2. $\{x \mid P_x \text{ or } Q_x\}$ or $\{x \mid P_x\} \cup \{x \mid Q_x\}$.

In mathematics we often encounter conditions such as

$$x \leq 4, \quad \text{and}$$
$$x \geq 5.$$

These are actually compound conditions because $x \leq 4$ means $x < 4$ *or* $x = 4$. Similarly $x \geq 5$ means $x > 5$ *or* $x = 5$. Consequently, the solution set of this new type of condition can be found through the union of two sets. For example, in the universe of real numbers, the solution set of $x \leq 4$ will be

$$\{x \mid x < 4\} \cup \{x \mid x = 4\},$$

which is the set of all real numbers less than, or equal to, 4.

The graph of this solution set is shown below.

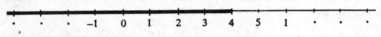

Fig. 41

The solution set of the compound condition $x \geq 5$ will be the set of all real numbers greater than, or equal to, 5.

The graph of this solution set is shown below.

Fig. 42

On occasion we have a condition expressed by an open sentence of the form $a < x < b$. The solution set can be determined by treating such a condition as a compound condition containing the connective *and*.

In the universe of real numbers let us consider a particular example such as $3 < x < 5$.

The solution set of this condition would be

$$\{x \mid 3 < x < 5\} = \{x \mid 3 < x \text{ and } x < 5\} \text{ or } \{x \mid 3 < x\} \cap \{x \mid x < 5\}.$$

The solution set for $3 < x$ is the set of real numbers greater than 3. The solution set of $x < 5$ is the set of real numbers less than 5. Therefore, the solution set of the compound condition $3 < x \text{ and } x < 5$ is the set of real numbers between 3 and 5.

Using graphs, the solution set of this compound condition can be illustrated as follows:

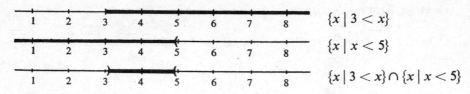

$\{x \mid 3 < x\}$

$\{x \mid x < 5\}$

$\{x \mid 3 < x\} \cap \{x \mid x < 5\}$

Fig. 43

QUADRATIC EQUATIONS

We shall now extend our discussion on conditions in one variable to quadratic (2nd degree) conditions. Let us consider the following illustrations:

1. $$x^2 + 5x + 6 = 0.$$
2. $$x^2 + 1 = 0.$$

The solution set of $x^2 + 5x + 6 = 0$ is

$$\{x \mid x^2 + 5 + 6 = 0\} \text{ or } \{x \mid (x + 2)(x + 3) = 0\} \text{ or } \{-2, -3\}.$$

The condition $(x + 2)(x + 3) = 0$ is equivalent to the compound condition $x + 2 = 0$ *or* $x + 3 = 0$. This is based on the theorem:

$$a \cdot b = 0 \text{ if, and only if, } a = 0 \text{ or } b = 0.$$

A formal proof of this theorem is given in Chapter 8.

Therefore, to obtain true statements from $x^2 = 5x + 6 = 0$, x must be replaced by -2 or -3. In other words the solution set is $\{-2, -3\}$.

The graph of the solution set of $x^2 + 5x + 6 = 0$ is shown below.

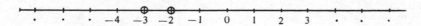

Fig. 44

The solution set of $x^2 + 1 = 0$ is the empty set since it is not possible to obtain a true statement from $x^2 + 1 = 0$ by replacing x by a real number.

A solution of $x^2 + 1 = 0$ is $\sqrt{-1}$ since $(\sqrt{-1})^2 + 1 = 0$.

But the $\sqrt{-1}$ is not a real number. It is a new number that is usually denoted by i, which when combined with real numbers produces another number system known as the complex number system. We shall not discuss this number system except to say that it is of great importance in advanced mathematics.

ABSOLUTE VALUES

In the universe of real numbers, let us consider three conditions that involve absolute value.

$$P_x: \quad |x| = 2.$$
$$Q_x: \quad |x| < 2.$$
$$R_x: \quad |x| > 2.$$

First let us review the definition of absolute value, which appeared on page 6 as follows:

The absolute value of x, written $|x|$, equals x if $x \geq 0$ or $-x$ if $x < 0$.

Therefore, in the condition $|x| = 2$, the variable x can be replaced by 2 or -2.
The solution set of P_x is

$$\{x \mid |x| = 2\} \text{ or } \{2, -2\}.$$

The graph of this solution set is shown below.

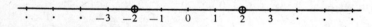

Fig. 45

The solution set of Q_x is

$$\{x \mid |x| < 2\} = \{x \mid x > -2 \ \ and \ \ x < 2\},$$
$$= \{x \mid x > -2\} \cap \{x < 2\},$$
$$= \text{the set of real numbers between } -2 \text{ and } 2.$$

The graph of this solution set is shown below.

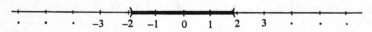

Fig. 46

The solution set of R_x is

$$\{x \mid |x| > 2\} = \{x \mid x > 2 \ \ or \ \ x < -2\},$$
$$= \{x \mid x > 2\} \cup \{x \mid x < -2\},$$
$$= \text{the set of all real numbers greater than 2 or less than } -2.$$

The graph of this solution set is shown below.

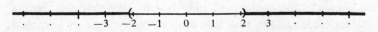

Fig. 47

The generalizations for the preceding three cases are as follows:

    1. If $|x| = a$, $a > 0$, then $x = a$ or $x = -a$.
    2. If $|x| < a$, $a > 0$, then $-a < x < a$.
    3. If $|x| > a$, $a > 0$, then $x > a$ or $x < -a$.

PROBLEMS FOR REVIEW

1. Using the universe $\{1, 2, 3, 4, 5, 6, 7, 8, 9, 10\}$, tabulate and then graph the solution sets of each of the conditions expressed below. Use the graph of the universe to help graph each solution set.

    (a) P_x: $x = 2$,
    (b) Q_x: $x + 3 = 9$,
    (c) R_x: $x > 4$,
    (d) T_x: $x < 6$.

2. If $A = \{x \mid x < 3\}$, and
     $B = \{x \mid x > 5\}$, and
     $U = D$, (the set of real numbers),
   graph (a) $A \cup B$,
        (b) $\overline{A \cup B}$.

3. Explain what is meant by saying that
$$\{x \mid x - 1 = x - 1\} = D.$$

4. Graph the solution set of each of the conditions expressed below in the universe of real numbers:

    (a) $x \leq -1$,
    (b) $1 < x < 4$,
    (c) $-2 \leq x \leq 2$.

5. Graph each of the following ($U = D$):

    (a) $\{x \mid x \geq 6\}$,
    (b) $\{x \mid x > 2 \text{ and } x < 4\}$,
    (c) $\{x \mid x > 2 \text{ or } x < 4\}$.

6. Graph the solution set of each of the following ($U = D$):

    (a) $2x + 1 = 4 \text{ or } x = 2$,
    (b) $3x - 2 = 7 \text{ or } x + 1 = 3$,
    (c) $3x + 2 > 14 \text{ and } x < 2$.

7. For each of the graphs below, describe the corresponding set of numbers.

(a)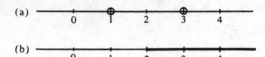

(b)

(c)

8. Tabulate and graph each of the following ($U =$ the set of integers):

(a) $\{x \mid 2 < x < 5\}$,

(b) $\{x \mid -2 \le x < 6\}$,

(c) $\{x \mid 3 \le x \le 4\}$.

BIBLIOGRAPHY

1. CHRISTIAN, ROBERT, R. *Introduction to Logic and Sets.* Toronto: Ginn and Company, 1958.

2. *Concepts of Equation and Inequality.* Commission on Mathematics. New York: College Entrance Examination Board, 1958.

3. KEMENY, J. G., SNELL, J. L. and THOMPSON, G. L. *Introduction to Finite Mathematics.* Chapter I. Englewood Cliffs, N.J.: Prentice Hall, Inc. 1957.

4. *Insights into Modern Mathematics.* 23rd Yearbook: National Council of Teachers of Mathematics, 1957, NCTM, Washington, D.C.

5 RELATIONS

In Chapter 4, we discussed conditions in one variable. In this chapter we shall concern ourselves with solution sets of conditions in two variables, such as

$$x + y = 4, \quad \text{and}$$
$$2a - 3 < b.$$

ORDERED PAIRS

We are familiar with pairs of objects, such as (bat, ball), (John Smith, Quarterback), (3, 5). When we list names of pairs of anything, the order in which the members are named is of great importance. For example, in making a list of the names of countries of Europe with their respective capitals, we might name the pairs as follows: Spain, Madrid; France, Paris; Italy, Rome; etc. In this set of pairs, Rome, Italy would be incorrect, because it would differ from the established pattern of country followed by capital. *A pair of things that occur in a specified order is called an ordered pair.*

The symbol (a, b) is used to denote the ordered pair consisting of a followed by b. The symbol (a, b) must not be confused with the symbol $\{a, b\}$. The symbol $\{a, b\}$ is used to denote a set having two members. This is a set of objects in which the order is not important. That is, $\{a, b\}$ is the same as $\{b, a\}$. But the ordered pair (a, b) is quite different from (b, a). This fact will be further clarified in the next few pages.

In previous chapters, we have been working with sets of objects or numbers. In this chapter, we shall be working with sets of ordered pairs of objects or numbers. The general symbol for a set of ordered pairs is

$$\{(a, b), (c, d) \ldots\}.$$

For example:

1. {(Spain, Madrid), (France, Paris), (Italy, Rome), . . .}.
2. {(1, 2), (2, 3), (3, 4), (4, 5), (5, 6)}.

Ordered pairs can be illustrated by means of graphs. In a situation where two variables are involved, we use rectangular coordinates for graphing. For example, if we wish to graph a problem involving distance and time, heights and weights, or any other problem situation involving two variables, we draw a horizontal line* and call it the first axis, and then we draw a line perpendicular to it and call it the second axis. We commence working from the point of intersection which is called the *origin*. Then we mark off a unit distance the desired number of times on each axis. Distances to the right of the origin (or to the right of the second axis) are positive, and distances to the left of the origin (or to the left of the second axis) are negative. Distances above the origin (or above the first axis) are positive, and distances below the origin (or below the first axis) are negative. Figure 48 illustrates the graphing of four points chosen at random.

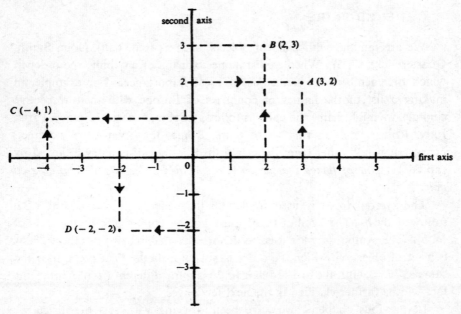

Fig. 48

---

* Actually, we do not draw a line. We draw a picture of a line, but for conciseness of language we will say "draw a line". Points and lines are abstract concepts and as such cannot be drawn. We can only draw pictures of them, or make representations of them.

Point A—3 units to the right of the second axis and 2 units above the first axis.

Point B—2 units to the right of the second axis and 3 units above the first axis.

Point C—4 units to the left of the second axis and 1 unit above the first axis.

Point D—2 units to the left of the second axis and 2 units below the first axis.

Observe that each point corresponds to an ordered pair of numbers. For example, A is designated as the point (3, 2). The 3 in the pair (3, 2) is the first component. It measures the directed distance from the second axis along the first axis (or along a line parallel to the first axis). The 2 in the pair (3, 2) is the second component. It measures the directed distance from the first axis along the second axis (or along a line parallel to the second axis). The two components for any point are called its coordinates. Therefore, the coordinates for point A are (3, 2), and the coordinates for points B, C, and D are as indicated in Figure 48.

We observe that point (3, 2) has a different location in the plane than does point (2, 3). In other words, the order of the numbers in such pairs is important; consequently, pairs of numbers used to designate points in a plane must be ordered pairs.

In algebra, the most common designation for an ordered pair is the symbol (x, y). Because the letters x and y are so frequently used in open sentences, most graphs in rectangular coordinates show the first axis as the x-axis and the second axis as the y-axis.

NON-MATHEMATICAL RELATIONS

Let us first consider a traditional non-mathematical meaning of the term relation such as "is the wife of", "is the brother of", or "is the uncle of". Expressing these relationships as open sentences, we have

y is the wife of x,

b is the brother of a,   and

n is the uncle of m.

Observe that the conditions expressed by these open sentences involve ordered pairs of variables. The true and full meaning of "is the wife of" cannot be appreciated without thinking of all married couples. That is to say, the term "is the wife of" expresses a relationship pertaining to a group or *set* of married couples. Similarly, other relationships such as this involve sets of ordered pairs.

We can exhibit sets of ordered pairs to illustrate such relations. Let us do this for the relation "*b* is the brother of *a*", e.g., {(Jane, Bill), (Peter, Tom), (Mary, Henry)}. Note that the ordered pair involved is (*a*, *b*).

MATHEMATICAL RELATIONS

We are now familiar with the meaning of ordered pairs of numbers. Suppose we consider the set of ordered pairs tabulated below:

$$\{(2, 4), (3, 9), (4, 16)\}.$$

Each of the pairs in this set will satisfy the condition "*y* is a multiple of *x*". That is, "4 is a multiple of 2", "9 is a multiple of 3", and "16 is a multiple of 4". This set of ordered pairs will also satisfy the condition "*y* is the square of *x*". Therefore, we can say "4 is the square of 2", "9 is the square of 3", and "16 is the square of 4". Consequently, we observe that more than one condition is satisfied by the same set of ordered pairs. Thus it is better and more precise to think of a relation in terms of a set of ordered pairs rather than a condition in two variables.

It should be clear that a *relation* can be defined most accurately in terms of sets, hence, we say *a relation is a set of ordered pairs.* Any set of ordered pairs is, therefore, a relation.* There are various ways in which we can express a relation:

1. By specifying or exhibiting a set of pairs, for example:
    (*a*) {(Mr. Jones, Mrs. Jones), (Mr. Smith, Mrs. Smith), (Mr. Brown, Mrs. Brown)}.
    (*b*) {(1, 2), (2, 3), (3, 4), (4, 5), (5, 6)}.

---

* Such relations are sometimes called *binary* relations to distinguish them from relations that involve more than two objects (or relata). In this book we shall be concerned only with binary relations. For convenience, therefore, the word *relation* will be understood to mean binary relation.

2. By standard description, using a rule or formula:

    (a) $\{(x, y) \mid 2x + y = 3\}$,

    (b) $\{(a, b) \mid 3a - b > 4\}$.

3. By tables, such as:

(a)

Country	France	England	Canada
Capital	Paris	London	Ottawa

(b)

x	2	4	6	8	10	12	14
y	5	8	11	14	17	20	23

4. By graphs:

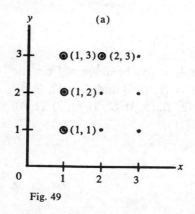
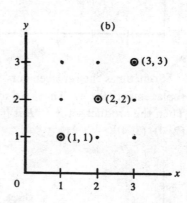

Fig. 49

CARTESIAN PRODUCTS

Before identifying some specific relations, let us clarify the meaning of universe. If we are working with the finite set, $A = \{1, 2, 3, 4\}$, the universe of discourse is the set consisting of all possible ordered pairs whose components belong to A. This set is denoted by $A \times A$ and we may write

$$A \times A = \{(x, y) \mid x \in A \text{ and } y \in A\}.$$

This is commonly known as the Cartesian product or simply the product set of A. The symbol $A \times A$ is read "A cross A".

$A \times A$ can be tabulated. It is the set of all ordered pairs that can be formed by selecting first components from A and second components from A.

$$A \times A = \{(1, 1),\ (1, 2),\ (1, 3),\ (1, 4),\ (2, 1),\ (2, 2),\ (2, 3),\ (2, 4),\ (3, 1),$$
$$(3, 2),\ (3, 3),\ (3, 4),\ (4, 1),\ (4, 2),\ (4, 3),\ (4, 4)\}.$$

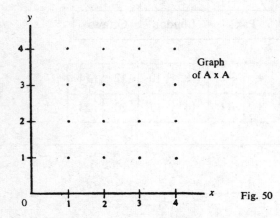

Graph of A x A

Fig. 50

Sometimes the replacements for the variable x may be different from the replacements for y. Thus, we might have $A = \{1, 2, 3\}$ and $B = \{2, 3, 4\}$. Then the product set $A \times B$ is $\{(1, 2), (2, 2), (3, 2), (1, 3), (2, 3), (3, 3), (1, 4), (2, 4), (3, 4)\}$.

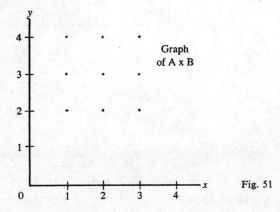

Graph of A x B

Fig. 51

Now let us consider some product sets that are infinite sets. If we are working with the natural numbers (N), the universe will be the set consisting of all possible ordered pairs whose components belong to N. This set is denoted by $N \times N$ and we may write

$$N \times N = \{(x, y) \mid x \in N \text{ and } y \in N\}.$$

$N \times N$ is the set of all pairs that can be formed by selecting first components from N and second components from N. For example, 0 is paired with each natural number, 0, 1, 2, ... Then 1 is paired with each natural number, 0, 1, 2, ... This creates an infinite set of ordered pairs that would be indicated as follows, using three dots (. . .) to stand for unlisted names:

$$N \times N = \{(0, 0), (0, 1), (0, 2), . . ., (4, 0), (4, 1), (4, 2), . . .\}.$$

If we are working with the set of integers (I), $I \times I$ is the set of all pairs that can be formed by selecting first components from I and second components from I. Similarly, using rationals (R), the product set is $R \times R$ and, using reals (D), the product set is $D \times D$.

We can summarize the preceding statements in the following table:

Set	Name	Name of Product Set
Natural numbers	N	$N \times N$
Integers	I	$I \times I$
Rationals	R	$R \times R$
Reals (decimal numbers)	D	$D \times D$

Subsets of a product set (such as $A \times A$, $A \times B$, $N \times N$, etc.) are relations. These subsets may be those that satisfy specific conditions in two variables, or they may be subsets chosen at random. Since both groups consist of subsets whose elements are ordered pairs, each subset in either group is a relation. Suppose $A = \{1, 2, 3\}$, and $B = \{1, 2, 3, 4\}$. Then $\{(2, 3), (2, 4), (1, 3)\}$ is a relation in $A \times B$. Many more relations (subsets) can be selected similarly at random from our product set $A \times B$.

CONDITIONS IN TWO VARIABLES

The following expresses a condition in two variables:

$$P_{xy}: \quad x + y = 4.$$

You recall that it is not appropriate to ask of a condition whether it is true or false in itself. Whereas a condition in one variable is true or false of individual numbers, a condition in two variables is true or false of pairs of numbers. It will be remembered, when we were working with conditions in one variable, that the variable could be replaced by any member of the universe in order to form statements. We noted that a solution set of a condition is the set of numbers that, upon replacement for the variable, make true statements from the condition.

Let us proceed to find the solution set of $x + y = 4$. It will be a subset of the universe. Suppose the universe is $A \times B$, where $A = \{1, 2, 3, 4, 5\}$ and $B = \{1, 2, 3, 4\}$; then $A \times B = \{(1, 1), (2, 1), (3, 1), (4, 1), (5, 1), (1, 2), (2, 2), (3, 2), (4, 2), (5, 2), (1, 3), (2, 3), (3, 3), (4, 3), (5, 3), (1, 4), (2, 4), (3, 4), (4, 4), (5, 4)\}$.

The graph of $A \times B$ is the *lattice* of points represented below.

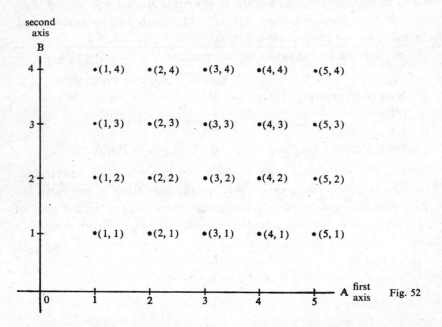

Fig. 52

We observe that twenty points are included in this lattice (Figure 52). Because A has five elements and B has four elements, $A \times B$ has five times four, or twenty, elements. The solution set consists of all those members of the universe (which in this case is a set of twenty ordered pairs) that form true statements from the condition. Since we are working again with sets, we shall use the notation and terminology developed in Chapter 4.

The solution set of $x + y = 4$ is $\{(x, y) \mid x + y = 4\}$. This may be read: The solution set of $x + y = 4$ is the set of ordered pairs (x, y) that satisfy the condition that $x + y = 4$. By replacement we observe that the solution set is $\{(1, 3), (2, 2), (3, 1)\}$. The graph of the solution set is indicated below. This graph shows the solution set *embedded* in the universe.

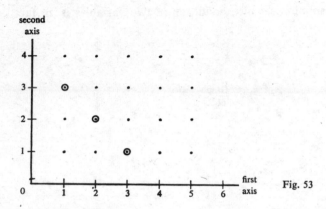

Fig. 53

Although we labelled each point in Figure 52 for clarification, we have labelled only the axes in Figure 53, which is common practice sufficient for our purpose.

It may be helpful here to review briefly the method used in reading a graph or locating a point. Suppose we wish to plot the point (a, b). We first count from the origin the number of unit distances indicated by the absolute value of a, to the right if $a > 0$, or to the left if $a < 0$. Then, along a vertical line that would pass through the point reached, we count the unit distances indicated by the absolute value of b, above this point if $b > 0$, or below this point if $b < 0$. The point reached is point (a, b). If we wish to determine the coordinates of a point on the graph, we reverse the operations and count the unit distances from the point back to the respective axes, and then determine whether the coordinates are positive or negative.

Let us now consider the conditions in two variables expressed below:

1. $y = x$.   2. $y < x$.   3. $y > x$.

We shall think of each of these conditions as defining a relation; in other words, each condition has a solution set that is a relation. Consider the condition $y = x$ as selecting from $A \times A$, where $A = \{1, 2, 3, 4, 5\}$, a subset of just those ordered pairs (x, y) for which the condition $y = x$ is satisfied. In this case the universe, $A \times A$, would be represented by a lattice of twenty-five points as shown below. The condition $y = x$ is satisfied for just five ordered pairs of $A \times A$. Thus, we can write $\{(x, y) \mid x = y\} = \{(1, 1), (2, 2),$ $(3, 3), (4, 4), (5, 5)\}$.

Figure 54 is the graph of R_1 (defined by $y = x$), embedded in the graph of the universe. (We shall usually denote relations by the letter R.) Thus we observe that the solution set of a condition in two variables is, in fact, a relation.

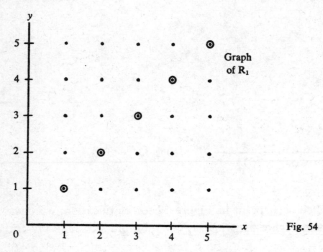

Fig. 54

Now let us consider the relation R_2 defined by $y < x$.

$R_2 = \{(x, y) \mid y < x\}$,
   $= \{(2, 1), (3, 1), (4, 1), (5, 1), (3, 2), (4, 2), (5, 2), (4, 3), (5, 3), (5, 4)\}$.

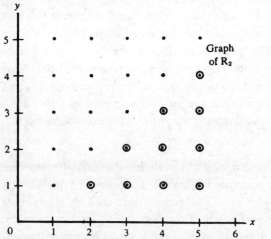

Fig. 55

The graph for R_2 is shown in Figure 55.

Now if we let R_3 be the relation defined by the sentence $y > x$, the graph appears in Figure 56.

$$R_3 = \{(x, y) \mid y > x\},$$
$$= \{(1, 2), (1, 3), (2, 3), (1, 4), (2, 4), (3, 4), (1, 5), (2, 5), (3, 5), (4, 5)\}.$$

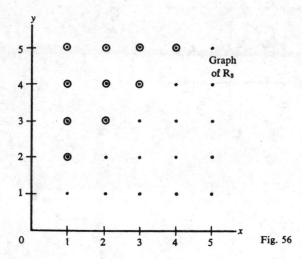

Graph of R_3

Fig. 56

Now let us consider different universes. If $A = \{-2, -1, 0, 1, 2\}$, the graph of the relation R_4 in $A \times A$ will be the graph of the ordered pairs contained in this relation as shown in Figure 57.

$$R_4 = \{(x, y) \mid y = x\},$$
$$= \{(-2, -2), (-1, -1), (0, 0), (1, 1), (2, 2)\}.$$

Suppose we consider the relation

$$R_5 = \{(x, y) \mid y = x\}, \text{ where } A = D.$$

Then the universe for (x, y) is $D \times D$, and the graph of R_5 is a diagonal line as shown in Figure 58.

Note that we have labelled this graph as being *incomplete*. Because we are working in the set of real numbers, the graph of R_5 extends indefinitely in both directions. In fact, if $A \times A$ is the product set of number pairs of any infinite set (naturals, rationals, integers, and reals), the graph must remain incomplete although it gives a meaningful, pictorial description of the relation in question.

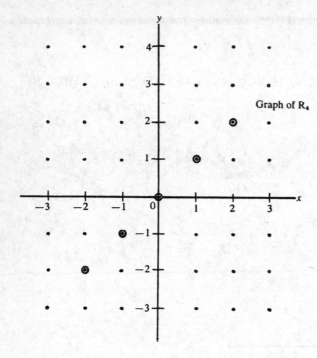

Graph of R₄

Fig. 57

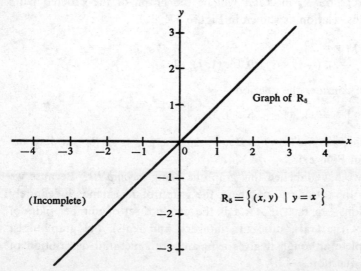

Graph of R_5

(Incomplete)

$R_5 = \left\{ (x, y) \mid y = x \right\}$

Fig. 58

Let us now consider the relation defined by the condition expressed below:

$$x^2 + y^2 < 4.$$

Let $A = \{-2, -1, 0, 1, 2\}$ and the universe be $A \times A$.

$R_6 = \{(x, y) \mid x^2 + y^2 < 4\}$,

= $\{(-1, -1), (0, -1), (1, -1), (-1, 0), (0, 0), (1, 0), (-1, 1), (0, 1), (1, 1)\}$.

The graph of R_6 is shown in Figure 59.

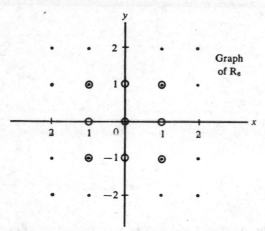

Fig. 59

COMMON RELATIONS IN SCHOOL
MATHEMATICS PROGRAMS

Let us now consider some relations defined by conditions that are studied in most school programs. In doing so, we shall encounter the familiar graphs of the straight line, the circle, and the parabola. To extend our experience, we shall study a relation whose graph is a square, and another relation whose graph is a rectangle.

Students of traditional mathematics get considerable practice in graphing conditions for equations, but very little experience in graphing conditions for inequalities. Graphs of several of the relations to follow depict conditions for inequalities. The first example is one of this type. We shall describe in some detail how to graph this relation in order that graphs of other relations will be understood more readily.

88 ✳

In the following examples the universe is $D \times D$.

EXAMPLE 1:

$$R_7 = \{(x, y) \mid y < x\}.$$

Let us go through the steps necessary to graph this relation. First, consider what the graph would be if the condition had been $y = x$. We have already discovered that this would be the diagonal straight line shown below.

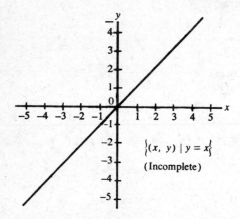

$\{(x, y) \mid y = x\}$

(Incomplete)

Fig. 60

We know, however, that the original condition is $y < x$. Let us consider the graphing of points that satisfy this condition. Suppose x is replaced by 2. We know that $y < x$, therefore we are looking for all y such that $y < 2$. Thus, y can be any real number less than 2. These numbers would correspond to all points in a line below the point (2, 2) in the following graph.

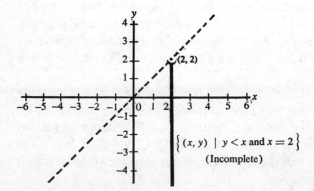

$\{(x, y) \mid y < x \text{ and } x = 2\}$

(Incomplete)

Fig. 61

Next, let us consider the replacement of x in $y = x$ by -2. On the graph of the diagonal, $y = -2$ when $x = -2$, but if we replace x by -2 in $y < x$, then y can be any real number less than -2. All possible replacements for y would correspond to all points in a line below the point $(-2, -2)$, as shown below.

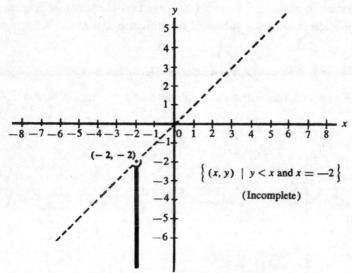

$$\{(x, y) \mid y < x \text{ and } x = -2\}$$

(Incomplete)

Fig. 62

If we continue to make other replacements for x in $y < x$, we shall discover that the graph of the condition $y < x$ is the region of the plane below the line ($y = x$). The graph of the relation $\{(x, y) \mid y < x\}$ is shown in Figure 63.

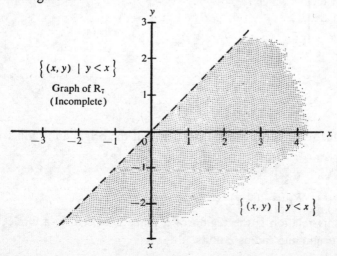

$$\{(x, y) \mid y < x\}$$

Graph of R_7
(Incomplete)

$$\{(x, y) \mid y < x\}$$

Fig. 63

The picture of the diagonal straight line is broken because it represents points which are not included in the graph of the relation under consideration. This practice will be followed in succeeding graphs under similar conditions.

No explanations of how to make the graphs will be given in the following examples. However, in each case it should be clear that the relation defined by a specific condition is always a subset of the universe $D \times D$.

EXAMPLE 2:

$$R_8 = \{(x, y) \mid y < x + 1\}.$$

The graph of this relation is the entire plane below the line $y = x + 1$.

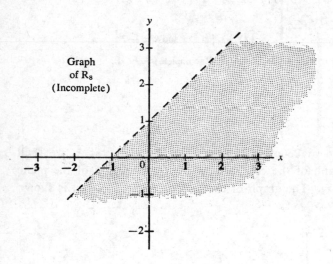

Graph
of R_8
(Incomplete)

Fig. 64

EXAMPLE 3:

$$R_9 = \{(x, y) \mid x^2 + y^2 = 4\}.$$

The graph of this relation is a circle with centre at the origin and radius 2 units.

EXAMPLE 4:

$$R_{10} = \{(x, y) \mid x^2 + y^2 < 4\}.$$

The graph of this relation is the region of a plane enclosed by a circle with centre at the origin and radius 2 units.

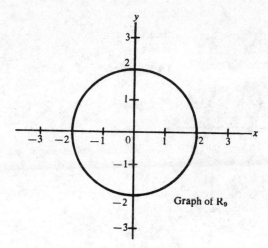

Graph of R$_9$

Fig. 65

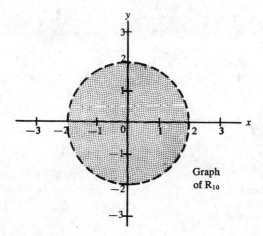

Graph
of R$_{10}$

Fig. 66

EXAMPLE 5:

$$R_{11} = \{(x, y) \mid x^2 + y^2 > 4\}.$$

The graph of R_{11} consists of all points exterior to the circle with centre at the origin and radius 2 units.

EXAMPLE 6:

$$R_{12} = \{(x, y) \mid y > x^2\}.$$

The graph of R_{12} consists of all points above the parabola.

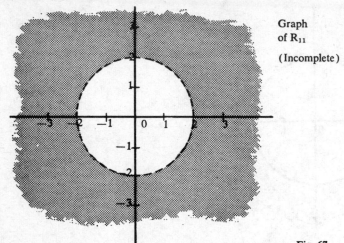

Graph
of R_{11}

(Incomplete)

Fig. 67

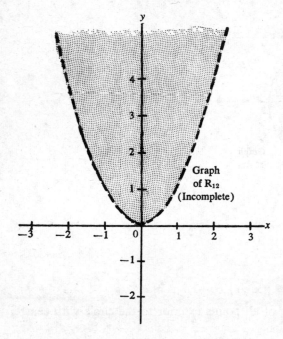

Graph
of R_{12}
(Incomplete)

Fig. 68

EXAMPLE 7:

$$R_{13} = \{(x, y) \mid y \geq -x^2\}.$$

The graph of R_{13} consists of all points in or above the parabola.

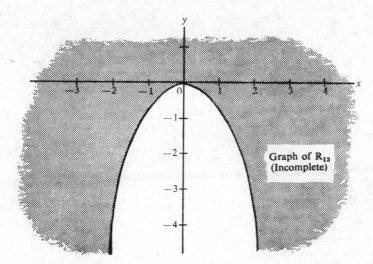

Graph of R_{13}
(Incomplete)

Fig 69

The following two examples are interesting relations defined by compound conditions.

EXAMPLE 8:

$$R_{14} = \{(x, y) \mid |x| + |y| \leq 1\}.$$

The graph of R_{14} is a square and region interior to the square.*

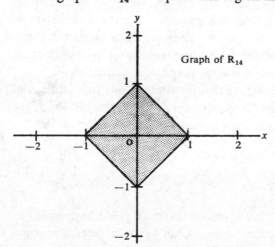

Graph of R_{14}

Fig. 70

* Comprehension of the meaning of absolute value is necessary to the understanding of R_{14}. From this, we proceed to find some ordered pairs that satisfy the condition for equality, i.e., $|x| + |y| = 1$, and locate these points. For example, when x is replaced by zero (0), we obtain (0, 1) and (0, −1) as solutions of $|x| + |y| = 1$. By making other replacements for x and y, other members of the solution set can be found. The graph of these points will yield a picture of the square. For the condition $|x| + |y| < 1$, all points (x, y) will be found interior to the square. The complete graph of this compound condition appears in Figure 70.

EXAMPLE 9:

$$R_{15} = \{(x, y) \mid 1 \leq x \leq 6 \quad \text{and} \quad 2 \leq y \leq 5\}.$$

The graph of R_{15} is a rectangle and region interior to the rectangle.

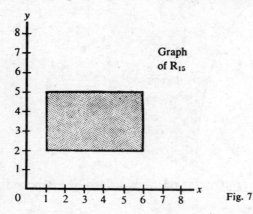

Graph
of R_{15}

Fig. 71

The preceding examples show that it is not difficult to graph a simple or compound condition in two variables. In order to graph a condition for inequality, we consider first the graph of the corresponding condition for equality. The graph of the condition for equality is usually a boundary of the graph of the condition for inequality. Once we have found the graph of the equation, the graph of the inequality consists of points that are interior to, exterior to, above, or below the graph of the equation.

From these illustrations we observe that the study of relations unifies and clarifies much of the work done in traditional mathematics, of which the graphing of equations and inequalities in two variables is an example.

SPECIFYING A RELATION

We recall that in Chapter 2 it was shown that a set could be specified by description (rule) or by tabulation. Any set can be so specified and, since it too is a set, a relation can be specified by rule or by tabulation. The only distinction between relations and the sets we discussed in Chapter 2 is that relations are sets of ordered pairs.

Suppose we have the condition $y = x^2$ and $A = \{1, 2, 3, 4, 5, 6, 7, 8, 9, 10\}$. The relation R in $A \times A$ may be specified by

$$R = \{(x, y) \mid y = x^2\}.$$

Here we specify the relation R by description or rule, since the description specifies just those ordered pairs that satisfy the condition $y = x^2$.

In our universe $A \times A$, there will be one hundred points in the graph of the Cartesian set, but only the following pairs, (1, 1), (2, 4), (3, 9), satisfy the condition. Therefore $R = \{(1, 1), (2, 4), (3, 9)\}$. R is specified by tabulation. In other words, we have listed between braces the names of all the ordered pairs in the relation R.

For the conditions expressed below, we shall specify the relation R determined for each condition by rule and by tabulation.

Let $A = \{1, 2, 3, 4\}$.

     $A \times A = \{(1, 1), (1, 2), (1, 3), \ldots (2, 1), (2, 2), (2, 3), \ldots (4, 4)\}$.

1. $x > y$.

     $R = \{(x, y) \mid x > y\}$.   (rule)

     $R = \{(2, 1), (3, 1), (4, 1), (3, 2), (4, 2), (4, 3)\}$. (tabulation)

2. $a = b$.

     $R = \{(a, b) \mid a = b\}$.   (rule)

     $R = \{(1, 1), (2, 2), (3, 3), (4, 4)\}$.   (tabulation)

3. $y = 2x$.

     $R = \{(x, y) \mid y = 2x\}$.   (rule)

     $R = \{(1, 2), (2, 4)\}$.   (tabulation)

We can reverse the process here, first tabulating a relation and then specifying it by a rule. For example, if $A =$ the set of natural numbers, we can have a relation

$$R = \{(1, 1), (2, 1), (1, 2)\}.$$

This gives the relation R by tabulation. The same relation could be described as

$$R = \{(x, y) \mid x + y < 4\}.$$

Before continuing, let us review the terminology that we use when speaking of relations, and at the same time summarize our ideas about them.

1. A relation is a set of ordered pairs.
2. A subset of $A \times B$ is called a relation in $A \times B$.
3. The graph of a relation R in $X \times Y$ is the subset of points in the graph of $X \times Y$ whose ordered pairs are in the relation R.
4. Relations may be defined by conditions.
5. Relations may be specified by tabulation or by rule.

DOMAIN AND RANGE OF A RELATION

Let us graph the relation as defined by $x + y < 5$ when $A \times B$ is the universe.

Where $A = \{1, 2, 3, 4, 5\}$ and $B = \{1, 2, 3, 4\}$,
$R = \{(x, y) \mid x + y < 5\}$,
$R = \{(1, 1), (2, 1), (3, 1), (1, 2), (2, 2), (1, 3)\}$.

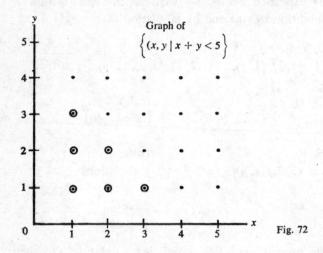

Graph of $\left\{(x, y \mid x + y < 5\right\}$

Fig. 72

Note that the graph of the product set $A \times B$ consists of twenty points and that the relation R is a subset of $A \times B$. To give further description of R, we say that the *domain of R* is the subset of A (or X, as the case may be) consisting of all *first* components of the ordered pairs belonging to R. The first components of the six ordered pairs belonging to R as tabulated above are 1, 2, 3, 1, 2, 1. Therefore we say the

$$\text{domain of } R = \{1, 2, 3\}.$$

The subset of B that consists of all *second* components of the ordered pairs belonging to R is called the *range of R*. In this case the

$$\text{range of } R = \{1, 2, 3\}.$$

We have graphed the relation defined by $y < x$ (R_2, Figure 55). Let us look at it again to observe the domain and range of the relation. ($A = \{1, 2, 3, 4, 5\}$.) (See Figure 73.)

The domain of $R = \{2, 3, 4, 5\}$, since this is the subset of A that consists of all *first* components of the ordered pairs in R.

The range of $R = \{1, 2, 3, 4\}$, as this is the subset of A that consists of all *second* components of the ordered pairs in R.

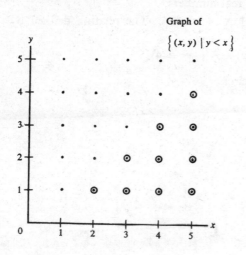

Graph of

$$\{(x, y) \mid y < x\}$$

Fig. 73

Domain and Range of Relations in $D \times D$

Most of our work in mathematics involves the universe $D \times D$, rather than a finite universe. Let us consider a couple of examples in $D \times D$, giving particular attention to the domain and range of the relations.

First let us examine the familiar condition $y = x^2$. Let

$$R = \{(x, y) \mid y = x^2\}.$$

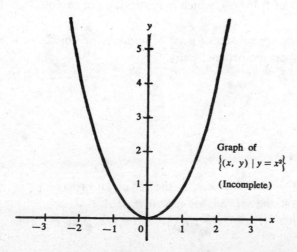

Graph of
$\{(x, y) \mid y = x^2\}$

(Incomplete)

Fig. 74

The graph of this relation is given in Figure 74.

The domain of this relation is the set of all real numbers (D). The range is the set of all non-negative real numbers.

Next let us study the condition $x^2 + y^2 = 4$. The relation defined by this condition is

$$R = \{(x, y) \mid x^2 + y^2 = 4\}.$$

The graph of this relation is a circle.

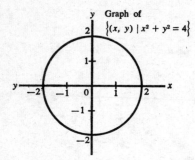

Fig. 75

The domain of R is $\{x \mid -2 \leq x \leq 2\}$ (-2 to 2, including -2 and 2). The range of R is $\{y \mid -2 \leq y \leq 2$ (-2 to 2, including -2 and 2).

The following points in this section are worthy of emphasis:

1. The domain is a subset of A (or X), which may or may not be equal to A (or X).

2. The range is a subset of B (or Y), which may or may not be equal to B (or Y).

3. The domain and range are subsets of a set of numbers or objects and are *not* subsets whose members are ordered pairs.

THE NOTATION yRx

The Cartesian set of A, which is $A \times A$, is the set of all ordered pairs whose components, both first and second, are members of A.

If $A = \{1, 2, 3, 4\}$, then $(1, 2) \in A \times A$, $(3, 4) \in A \times A$, but $(4, 6) \notin A \times A$ and $(7, 3) \notin A \times A$.

Now if we specify a relation

$$R = \{(x, y) \mid P_{xy}\},*$$

we can then write $\{(x, y) \in R\}$, to indicate those pairs that are contained in R.

This can be expressed by the notation yRx, which is read "y is related to x through R".

It may seem more natural to write xRy. In fact, this notation is used on occasion. However, we shall choose to use yRx for these mathematical reasons:

1. The relation R consists of the ordered pairs (x, y) where x is contained in the domain and y in the range. By assigning values to x we determine corresponding values for y. It follows that y is related to x through R, hence the notation yRx.

2. The relation defined by an equation such as $y = x^2$ is

$$R = \{(x, y) \mid y = x^2\}.$$

Here $\{(x, y) \in R\}$ means yRx, since y is the square of x. In this example, R stands for "is the square of".

3. We always relate the range to the domain, which again suggests the notation yRx.

If R is the relation "is greater than", then we might have

$$R = \{(x, y) \mid y > x\}.$$

If one of the ordered pairs in this relation is $(4, 7)$, we say that $(4, 7) \in R$, but $7R4$ means 7 is greater than 4.

Further reference will be made to the notation yRx in the chapter on FUNCTIONS.

In yRx, R might stand for "is greater than". In different situations it can stand for different relations, non-mathematical as well as mathematical. Following are some relations that can be designated by R in yRx:

1. "is greater than"
2. "is less than"
3. "equals"
4. "is the wife of"
5. "is the father of"
6. "is the divisor of"

* The notation P_{xy} expresses any condition in two variables.

For example:

If "y is a divisor of x" in $A \times A$, we could write

$$R = \{(x, y) \mid y \text{ is a divisor of } x\}.$$

If $A =$ the set of natural numbers (N), then the symbols

$$(9, 3) \in R, (4, 2) \in R, (8, 4) \in R.$$

can be written in the yRx notation as follows:

$$3R9, \ 2R4, \ 4R8.$$

The R stands for "is a divisor of".

EQUIVALENCE RELATIONS

Relations may be classified according to certain special properties. The following properties are of particular interest and importance.

1. A relation R is said to be *reflexive*, if xRx for all elements of the domain of R. That is, if R relates every element of the domain to itself, R is reflexive. For example, the relation "is as strong as" is reflexive, since every member x of the domain must be as strong as itself.

2. A relation R is said to be *symmetric* when, if yRx, then xRy for all x in the domain of R and all y in the range of R. For example, the relation "weighs the same as" is symmetric; if y weighs the same as x, then x weighs the same as y.

3. A relation R is said to be *transitive*, if xRy and yRz, then xRz. For example, the relation "has the same area as" is transitive; if x has the same area as y, and y has the same area as z, then x has the same area as z.

Relations may possess *none* of these properties. For example, the relation "is the mother of" is neither reflexive, symmetric, or transitive. This fact is clear since x cannot be his own mother; and if x is the mother of y, y cannot be the mother of x; and finally if x is the mother of y, and y is the mother of z, x cannot be the mother of z.

Relations may possess only *one* of these properties, which indicates that no one of these properties follows as a consequence of one or both of the other two. For example, the relation "is three miles from" is symmetric, but neither reflexive nor transitive. If x is three miles from y, y is three miles from x (symmetric), but x cannot be three miles from itself; and if x is three miles from y, and y is three miles from z, x is not likely to be three miles from z.

Relations may possess only *two* of these properties. Let us consider the relation "is a divisor of" in the universe of natural numbers (N). Any natural number is a divisor of itself (reflexive). If x is a divisor of y and y is a divisor of z, then x is a divisor of z (transitive). However, if x is a divisor of y, and $x \neq y$, y cannot be a divisor of x. For example, if x is 3, and y is 12, 3 is a divisor of 12, but 12 cannot be a divisor of 3 in the universe of natural numbers. Therefore, we conclude that the relation "is a divisor of" is reflexive and transitive but not symmetric.

Finally, relations may possess all *three* of these properties. For example, the relation "is congruent to" is reflexive, symmetric and transitive. Consider three triangles, x, y, and z. The triangle x is congruent to itself. If x is congruent to y, y is congruent to x. Furthermore, if x is congruent to y, and y is congruent to z, then x is congruent to z. Relations that possess all three of these properties are known as *equivalence relations*. An equivalence relation is defined as follows:

> *R is an equivalence relation just in case R is reflexive, symmetric, and transitive.*

The relation "is equal to" ($=$) is one of the most important equivalence relations in mathematics. Let us show that "is equal to" is an equivalence relation in the universe of natural numbers (N). Any natural number is equal to itself (xRx—reflexive); if a natural number y is equal to a natural number x, then x is equal to y (if yRx then xRy—symmetric). Also, if a natural number x is equal to a natural number y, and y is equal to a natural number z, then x is equal to z (if xRy and yRz, then xRz—transitive). Hence, the relation "is equal to" ($=$) is an equivalence relation. Similarly, we could show that ($=$) is an equivalence relation in another universe, such as the set of integers.

A Use of the Equivalence Relation

Equivalence relations play a most significant rôle in mathematics because of the fact that an equivalence relation partitions the universe into disjoint subsets whose union is the whole universe. Let us consider first the relation "is similar to" in the universe of triangles. This equivalence relation separates all triangles into disjoint sets with respect to shape (similarity). One subset of the universe of triangles is all equilateral triangles; another subset is all right-angled isosceles triangles, etc.

Each triangle in the universe falls into exactly one subset. Consequently the union of all the subsets of the set of triangles is equal to the universe of triangles.

Using an equivalence relation over the set of fractions, we can partition all fractions into disjoint sets. We shall define the fraction a/b to be equivalent to c/d just in case $ad = bc$. Now using this equivalence relation, we shall partition our universe. We do so by first selecting a fraction, such as $1/3$. Other fractions equivalent to $1/3$ are $2/6$, $3/9$, $4/12$, etc., which form the set

$$A = \{1/3, 2/6, 3/9, 4/12 \ldots n/3n \ldots\}.$$

Note that each member of A is equivalent to $n/3n$. Similarly we can form the set

$$B = \{5/4, 10/8, 15/12 \ldots 5n/4n \ldots\}.$$

Here each member of B is equivalent to $5n/4n$.

We might continue this process indefinitely, but we should find that no fraction would appear in more than one subset. We conclude, therefore, that the special equivalence relation defined above partitions the universe of fractions into disjoint sets.

THE ALGEBRA OF RELATIONS

The application of set theory to relations will help us to broaden our understanding of relations. We have seen that a relation is a set of ordered pairs. If the set is empty, we have an empty or *null relation*. On the other hand, if every member of the Cartesian set is included in the relation we have a *universal relation*. Finally, the subset of all ordered pairs in $A \times A$ that are not in the relation is called the *complementary relation*.

Under the heading "Operations on Sets" in Chapter 2, we learned of intersection, union, and complement. We shall now apply these ideas to relations. Let us use relations R_1 and R_2 for purposes of illustration.

Let $A = \{1, 2, 3\}$.

Then $A \times A = \{(1, 1), (1, 2), (1, 3), (2, 1), (2, 2), (2, 3), (3, 1), (3, 2), (3, 3)\}$.

Intersection

$R_1 \cap R_2 =$ the set consisting of just those members that belong to both R_1 and R_2. Since R_1 and R_2 are disjoint sets, there are no members in the

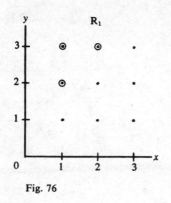
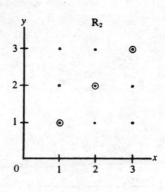

Fig. 76

intersection of R_1 and R_2. Therefore we can say that $R_1 \cap R_2$ is the *null* relation.

Union

$R_1 \cup R_2 =$ the set consisting of just those members of $A \times A$ which belong either to R_1 or to R_2 or to both. (Usually, the phrase "or to both" is omitted, since in mathematics it is implied by "or"). Therefore, the graph of $R_1 \cup R_2$ is:

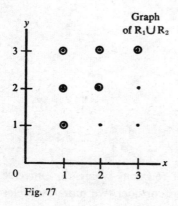

Graph of $R_1 \cup R_2$

Fig. 77

Complement

The complement of R_1, which may be designated as $\bar{R}_1 =$ the set consisting of just those members of $A \times A$ that are not in the relation. The graph for the complement of R_1 is shown on page 104.

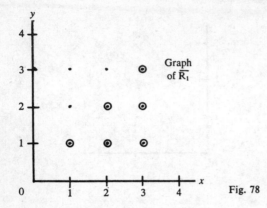

Fig. 78

The graph of the complement of $R_1 \cup R_2$, designated as $\overline{R_1 \cup R_2}$, is:

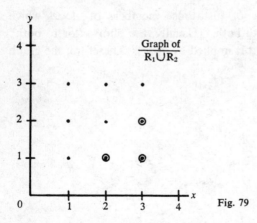

Fig. 79

We have been considering the algebra of relations where the universe was $A \times A$ as defined on page 102. Now let us consider two more examples of the algebra of relations in which the universe is $D \times D$.

Suppose we have the two relations that follow:

$$R_3 = \{(x, y) \mid x = y^2\}, \quad \text{and}$$
$$R_4 = \{(x, y) \mid x = 4\}.$$

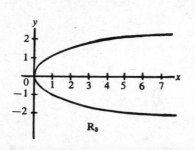

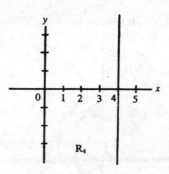

R₃

R₄

Fig. 80

The graph of the intersection of R_3 and R_4 is shown below. Note that the graph consists of just two points.

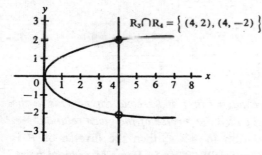

$$R_3 \cap R_4 = \left\{ (4, 2), (4, -2) \right\}$$

Fig. 81

Finally, if we are given the relations

$$R_5 = \{(x, y) \mid x^2 + y^2 \leq 4\}, \quad \text{and}$$
$$R_6 = \{(x, y) \mid x + y \leq 2\},$$

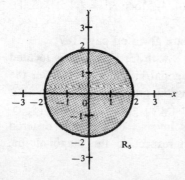

R₅

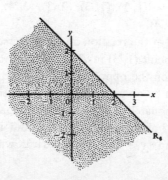

R₆

Fig. 82

the graph of the union, $R_5 \cup R_6$, would then be :

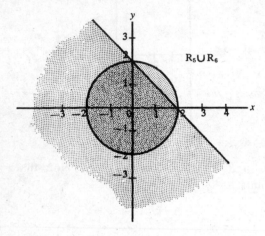

Fig. 83

INVERSE OF A RELATION

The relation obtained by interchanging first and second components in the ordered pairs of a given relation is called the inverse of the given relation.

For example, if R is any relation in $A \times A$, then the inverse of R is denoted by R^i (which is read "R inverse"). Then in terms of ordered pairs, we have

$$(y, x) \in R^i \text{ just in case } (x, y) \in R.$$

For example,

$$(1, 2) \in R^i \text{ just in case } (2, 1) \in R, \quad \text{and}$$
$$(2, 4) \in R^i \text{ just in case } (4, 2) \in R.$$

Suppose $R = \{(1, 1), (1, 3), (2, 3), (3, 4), (4, 4)\}$, then $R^i = \{(1, 1), (3, 1), (3, 2), (4, 3), (4, 4)\}$.

The graphs of the relation and its inverse are given on page 107.

Note that point $(1, 3)$ in R is matched in R with $(3, 1)$, which is located symmetrically on the opposite side of the diagonal line $y = x$. In fact, the graph of R can be obtained simply by rotating the graph of R through $180°$ about the diagonal line $y = x$ so that point (x, y) goes into point (y, x). This property holds for any relation and its inverse, because the ordered pairs (x, y) and (y, x) are symmetrical with respect to the diagonal line $y = x$.

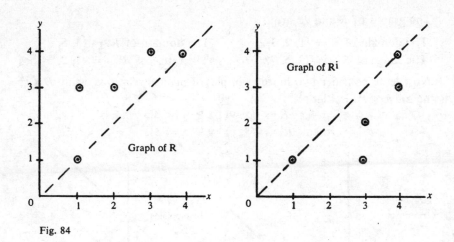

Fig. 84

Suppose a relation R is defined by a condition P_{xy} in the following manner:

$$R = \{(x, y) \mid P_{xy}\}.$$
$$\text{If so, then } R^i = \{(x, y) \mid P_{yx}\}.$$

For example, suppose $P_{xy}: y = 2x + 1$, when $A = \{1, 2, 3, 4, 5, 6, 7, 8\}$ and $A \times A$ is the universe. Then,

$$R = \{(x, y) \mid y = 2x + 1\},$$
$$= \{(1, 3), (2, 5), (3, 7)\}, \quad \text{and}$$
$$R^i = \{(x, y) \mid x = 2y + 1\},$$
$$= \{(3, 1), (5, 2), (7, 3)\}.$$

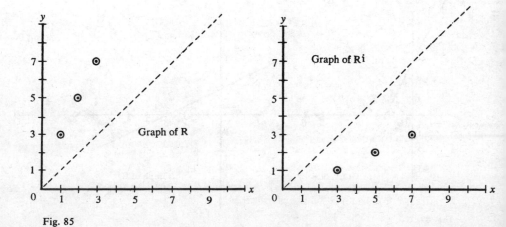

Fig. 85

The graphs of R and R^i are:

The domain of $R = \{1, 2, 3\}$.   The domain of $R^i = \{3, 5, 7\}$.
The range of $R\ \ = \{3, 5, 7\}$.   The range of $R^i\ \ = \{1, 2, 3\}$.

Now let us consider two more examples of inverse relations, using $D \times D$ as the universe. First let

$$R = \{(x, y) \mid x - y = 3\},$$
$$\text{then}\quad R^i = \{(x, y) \mid y - x = 3\}.$$

Fig. 86

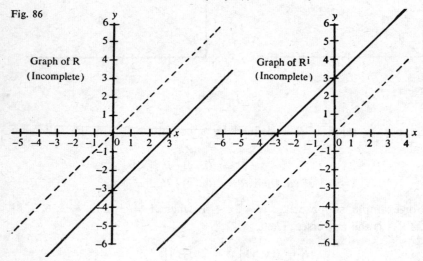

Graph of R
(Incomplete)

Graph of R^i
(Incomplete)

Finally, let

$$R = \{(x, y) \mid 2x + y = 3\},$$
$$\text{then}\quad R^i = \{(x, y) \mid 2y + x = 3\}.$$

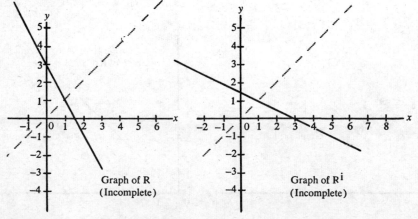

Graph of R
(Incomplete)

Graph of R^i
(Incomplete)

Fig. 87

The foregoing graphs and many others, where the universe is $D \times D$, are necessarily incomplete.

PROBLEMS FOR REVIEW

1. Suppose A is a set such that $A \times A$ has nine members and two of the pairs in $A \times A$ are (3, 4) and (4, 5). Tabulate the product set $A \times A$.

2. (a) Let $A = \{1, 2\}$ and $B = \{a, b, c\}$. Tabulate and graph $A \times B$.
   (b) How many members has the product set $A \times A$ in each of the following cases?

   i. $A = \{x_1, x_2\}$,
   ii. $A = \{a_1, a_2, a_3, \ldots a_n\}$.

3. If $A = \{1, 2, 3, 4\}$, which of the ordered pairs in $A \times A$ satisfy the condition expressed by each of the following open sentences:

   (a) y is a divisor of x,
   (b) x is a divisor of y,
   (c) $x + y = 5$,
   (d) $y = x - 1$.

4. In the universe of $N \times N$, graph the relations expressed below:

   (a) $R_1 = \{(x, y) \mid y^2 = 2x\}$,
   (b) $R_2 = \{(x, y) \mid x^2 + y^2 > 16\}$.

5. Which of the following relations are symmetric? reflexive? transitive?

   (a) "is a sister of",
   (b) "loves",
   (c) "is less than",
   (d) "intersects",
   (e) "is parallel to".

6. (a) Let R be a relation in $D \times D$, whose domain is $\{3\}$ and whose range is D. Graph R.
   (b) Suppose R_1 is a relation in $D \times D$, whose domain is $\{D\}$ and whose range is $\{-2\}$. Graph R_1.

7. Graph the relation $R = \{(x, y) \mid y^2 = x + 1\}$ in the following universes. Specify the domain and the range of the relation in each case.

    i. $N \times N$,

    ii. $I \times I$,

    iii. $D \times D$.

8. What relation of the form $\{(x, y) \mid \ldots\}$ will yield the region of the plane:

    (a) included in the first quadrant?

    (b) above the first axis?

    (c) to the right of the second axis?

9. If $A = \{1, 2, 3, 4\}$, consider the following relations in $A \times A$.

$$R_1 = \{(x, y) \mid x + y < 5\}.$$
$$R_2 = \{(x, y) \mid x = 3\}.$$

    (a) Tabulate and graph R_1, R_2, R_1^i, $R_1 \cap R_2$, $R_1 \cup R_2$, $\overline{R_1 \cup R_2}$.

    (b) Tabulate the domain and range for each of the relations in (a).

10. Consider the following relations in $D \times D$.

$$R_1 = \{(x, y) \mid y = x\}.$$
$$R_2 = \{(x, y) \mid y > x\}.$$
$$R_3 = \{(x, y) \mid y \geq x\}.$$

Using graphs, show that

    (a) $R_2 \subseteq R_3$.

    (b) $R_1 \cup R_2 = R_3$.

BIBLIOGRAPHY

1. ALLENDOERFER, C. B. and OAKLEY, C. A. *Principles of Mathematics*. New York: McGraw-Hill Book Company, 1952.

2. *Sets, Relations, and Functions*. Commission on Mathematics of the College Entrance Examination Board, 1958.

3. *Sentences, Relations*. Mathematics Staff of the College: University of Chicago, 1956.

4. *Insights into Modern Mathematics*. 23rd Yearbook: National Council of Teachers of Mathematics, 1957. NCTM, Washington, D.C.

5. *The Growth of Mathematical Ideas, Grades K—12*. 24th Yearbook: National Council of Teachers of Mathematics, 1959. NCTM, Washington, D.C.

6 FUNCTIONS

Certain relations that we have considered differ from others in at least one respect. In some relations the first element of each ordered pair in the relation is paired with only one second element. In other words, for each element of the domain there corresponds one and only one element of the range. This type of relation is known in mathematics as a *function*. Thus *a function is a set of ordered pairs, no two of which have the same first component.* Let us illustrate this point by looking at some graphs of relations.

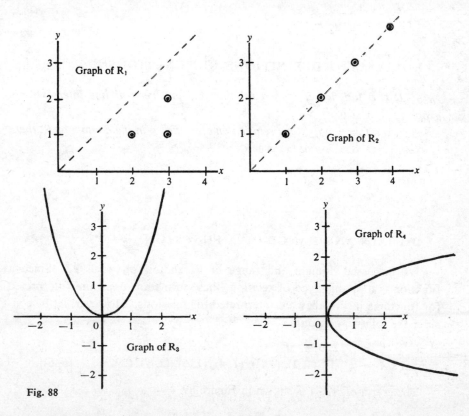

Fig. 88

The precise graphical test of a function is as follows:

R is a function if R is a relation and if each vertical line intersects the graph of R in at most one point.

The significance of this definition is simply this. If a vertical line intersects the graph of a relation more than once, there would have to be at least two points of the graph of the relation in this vertical line. In order for this to be true, the points in question must have the same first component. If this were true, R could not be a function, since if R is a function no two ordered pairs have the same first component.

Applying this graphical test to the four relations, R_1, R_2, R_3, and R_4, we note that R_2 and R_3 are functions, but that R_1 and R_4 are not functions. There are two points in the graphs of R_1 and R_4 that are in the same vertical line, whereas in the graphs of R_2 and R_3 no two points are located along the same vertical line and, therefore, only R_2 and R_3 are functions.

EQUIVALENT DEFINITIONS OF FUNCTIONS

1. *R is a function if R is a relation and any vertical line intersects the graph of R in at most one point.*
2. *R is a function if R is a relation and for each x in the domain of R, there is exactly one y such that $(x, y) \in R$.*

DOMAIN AND RANGE OF A FUNCTION

We discussed domain and range of a relation on page 97. Since a function is a special type of relation, these terms are used and interpreted for functions just as they are interpreted for relations. However, let us consider the following examples.

If $A = \{1, 2, 3, 4, 5\}$,
then $A \times A = \{(1, 1), (1, 2), (1, 3), (1, 4), (1, 5), (2, 1), (2, 2) \ldots (5, 5)\}$.

The graph of $A \times A$ is shown in Figure 89.

1. Let $R = \{(x, y) \mid x + y = 4\}$.
   Then $R = \{(1, 3), (2, 2), (3, 1)\}$ (Figure 90).

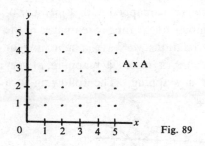

Fig. 89

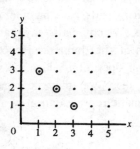

Fig. 90

Since each element of the domain belongs to only one pair of components, this relation is a function. It may be denoted by F.

Domain of $F = \{1, 2, 3\}$,   and the
Range of F $= \{1, 2, 3\}$.

2. $R = \{(x, y) \mid 2y = 3x + 1\}$ in $D \times D$.

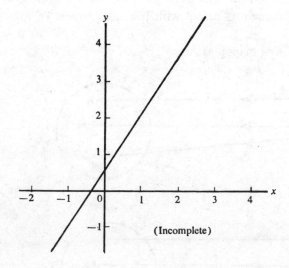

(Incomplete)

Fig. 91

The domain of $R =$ set of all real numbers (D).
The range of $R =$ set of all real numbers (D).

FUNCTIONS DEFINED AS MAPPINGS

In our study of relations we observed that yRx meant that $(x, y) \in R$ and that we assign values to x and then determine corresponding values for y. In other words, each member of the domain is mapped onto a member of the range. We could also say that the members of the range are images of the members of the domain. Hence, in all relations we have a matching or pairing-off operation which, as we have said, is called a mapping. Every relation, therefore, may be regarded as a mapping. The following is a diagrammatic representation of a mapping:

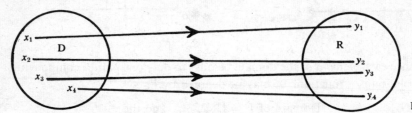

Fig. 92

The domain (D) is a set that is mapped onto the range (R). If an element of the domain maps onto two or more elements of the range, the relation is not a function. The relation shown in Figure 92 is a function since each element of the domain maps onto just one element of the range. In other words, each element of the domain is paired with just one element of the range.

Let us consider the following mappings:

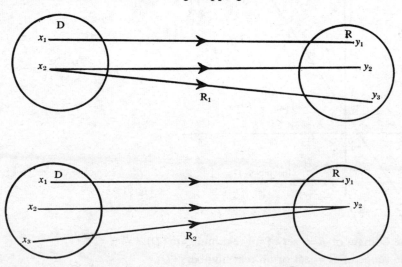

Fig. 93

For R_1 the domain is $\{x_1, x_2\}$ and the range is $\{y_1, y_2, y_3\}$. Its graph is shown in Figure 94.

This relation is not a function since x_2 is paired with y_2 and y_3 (more than one element of the range).

For R_2 the domain is $\{x_1, x_2, x_3\}$ and the range is $\{y_1, y_2\}$. The graph of R_2 is shown in Figure 95.

This relation is a function since each element of the domain is paired with just one element of the range.

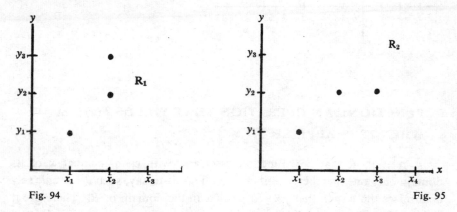

Fig. 94   Fig. 95

Furthermore, since two elements x_2, x_3 of the domain of R_2 are mapped onto one element y_2 of the range of R_2, we have a many-to-one mapping. From this, we learn that whenever we map the domain of a relation onto the range of the same relation and get a many-to-one mapping, we know that the relation is a function. We observe, of course, that a one-to-one mapping is a special case of a many-to-one mapping and, hence, that it also generates a function.

Let us consider another example of a many-to-one mapping. Suppose

$$F = \{(x, y) \mid y = 2\}.$$

As a mapping this function may be illustrated as follows:

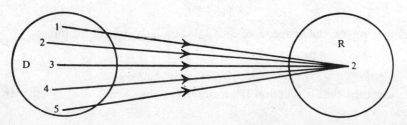

Fig. 96

Its graph is shown in Figure 97.

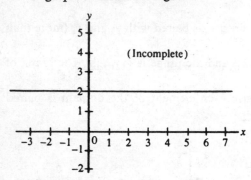

Fig. 97

FUNCTION: AN OPERATION THAT YIELDS $F(x)$
WHEN IT IS APPLIED TO x

A relation R that is a function associates with each member x of its domain only one member y of its range. That is to say, such an R uniquely determines the y such that yRx for each x in the domain of R. Therefore it is convenient to use a special notation for relations that are functions. Instead of yRx, we write $y = F(x)$. Note that such a notation can not be used for any other type of relation, because the y is not uniquely determined in a non-functional relation, since more than one ordered pair may have the same first component.

Let us consider the function F in $D \times D$ such that

$$yFx \text{ just in case } y = 3x + 2.$$

Since we are working in $D \times D$, each real number is in the domain. Suppose we select the number 3. The image of 3 is $F(3)$, read "F of 3". In this example $F(3) = 11$, since by replacing x by 3 in the equation $y = 3x + 2$, we get

$$y = 3(3) + 2,$$
$$= 11.$$

In other words, the image, F of 3, is 11. Similarly, in this example:

$$F(2) = 8. \quad \text{(The image, } F \text{ of 2, is 8.)}$$
$$F(1) = 5. \quad \text{(The image, } F \text{ of 1, is 5.)}$$

We say then that a function is an operation that yields $F(x)$ when it is applied to x.

INVERSE FUNCTIONS

In mathematics it is often necessary to consider the set of ordered number pairs formed by interchanging the first and second components of each pair in a given set. We noted in Chapter 5 that when this is done for the ordered pairs of a relation we get the inverse of the given relation. Since all functions are relations, it follows that we can have the inverse of a function. The inverse of a function F is denoted by F^i (which is read "F inverse").

The relation F^i is defined as follows: $(y, x) \in F^i$ just in case $(x, y) \in F$. For example:

$$(2, 3) \in F^i \text{ just in case } (3, 2) \in F, \text{ and}$$
$$(3, 5) \in F^i \text{ just in case } (5, 3) \in F.$$

Suppose we indicate a function F by the following tabulation:

$$F = \{(1, 1), (2, 3), (3, 5), (4, 7)\}.$$

Then the inverse F^i is

$$F^i = \{(1, 1), (3, 2), (5, 3), (7, 4)\}.$$

The graphs of this function and its inverse are shown in Figure 98.

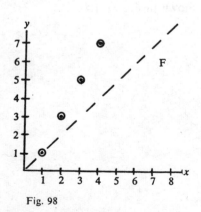 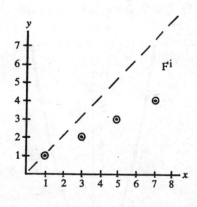

Fig. 98

We note here that the points associated with a function and its inverse are located symmetrically on opposite sides of the diagonal. As in the case for the inverse of a relation, the graph of the inverse of a function can be obtained by rotating the graph of F about the diagonal line $y = x$, so that the point (x, y) goes into the point (y, x).

It should be observed that the inverse of the function F above is itself a function because it satisfies the definition of a function. However, the inverse of a function is not always a function. Let us consider the following example:

Suppose the function is defined by rule as follows:

$$F = \{(x, y) \mid y = x^2\}.$$

The graph of this function, in $I \times I$, is shown in Figure 99.

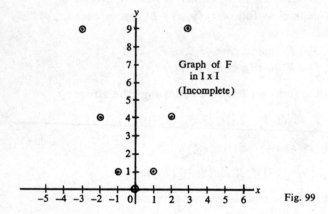

Graph of F
in I x I
(Incomplete)

Fig. 99

In $D \times D$, the graph of this function is shown in Figure 100.

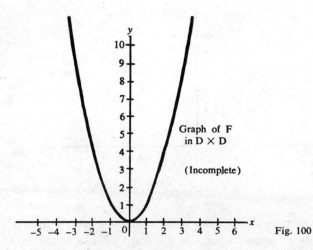

Graph of F
in D × D
(Incomplete)

Fig. 100

If we interchange the components in each ordered pair of the foregoing function and draw a graph using this new set of ordered pairs, we get a graph of the inverse of this function. If we rotate the graph of the function about the diagonal line $y = x$, we get the graph of the inverse of this function. In either case it would, of course, take the form shown in Figure 101.

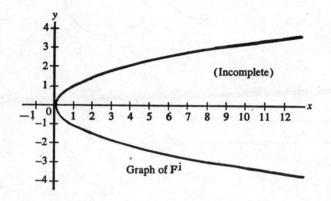

(Incomplete)

Graph of F^i

Fig. 101

This inverse is not a function since a line drawn vertically through its graph would intersect the graph more than once. In case the relation F^i, inverse to F, is also a function, F is known as a *one-to-one function*. Note that in a one-to-one function each member of the range is the image of exactly one member of the domain.

In terms of mapping, the inverse of a relation is the mapping that goes the other way. In other words, it is a reverse mapping. Suppose the function F is specified by the following set of ordered pairs:

$$F = \{(x_1, y_1), (x_2, y_3), (x_3, y_3)\}.$$

The mappings of F and F^i are shown in Figure 102.

Note that F is not a one-to-one function since F^i is not a function. The two ordered pairs (y_3, x_2) and (y_3, x_3), have the same first component. Thus, F^i is not a function.

ALGEBRA OF RELATIONS

In Chapter 3 we discussed operations on sets. We can have similar operations on relations. Although the algebra of relations was treated

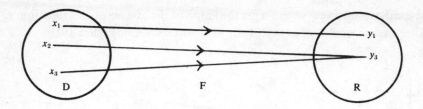

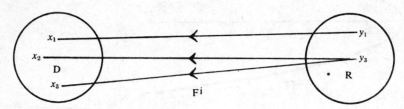

Fig. 102

briefly in Chapter 5, we shall now give a few more examples of operations on relations to extend our understanding and use of them.

Let us first consider some examples that illustrate the operation of forming the intersection. In each example, we shall let the universe be $D \times D$.

1. Let $F_1 = \{(x, y) \mid x + y = 4\}$, and
$F_2 = \{(x, y) \mid x - y = 2\}$.

Suppose we wish to find a replacement for x and a replacement for y that will satisfy both conditions. In the traditional approach, we proceed as follows:

$$x + y = 4.$$
$$x - y = 2.$$

Adding, we get $2x = 6$ or $x = 3$. Replacing x by 3 in these equations, we get $y = 1$. The solution of this system of equations is (3, 1).

Operating with sets, we recognize this problem as one of intersection. We want to find $F_1 \cap F_2$,

$$\{(x, y) \mid x + y = 4 \quad and \quad x - y = 2\} =$$
$$\{(x, y) \mid x + y = 4\} \cap \{(x, y) \mid x - y = 2\} = F_1 \cap F_2.$$

The graph on page 121 determines the solution set of $F_1 \cap F_2$.

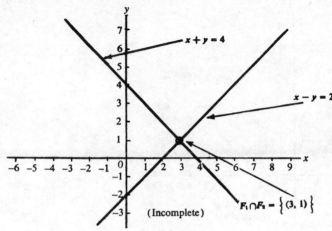

Fig. 103

Thus, we observe that set notation enables us to develop a richer understanding of systems of equations. We see that a system of equations is actually a compound condition involving the connective *and*. We recall that

$$\{(x, y) \mid P_{xy} \text{ and } Q_{xy}\} = \{(x, y) \mid P_{xy}\} \cap \{(x, y) \mid Q_{xy}\}.$$

Hence, we see a reason for selecting the coordinates of the point of intersection as the only member of our solution set.

2. Let $R_3 = \{(x, y) \mid x + y > 4\}$, and
$R_4 = \{(x, y) \mid x - y < 2\}$.
$\{(x, y) \mid x + y > 4 \quad and \quad x - y < 2\} =$
$\{(x, y) \mid x + y > 4\} \cap \{(x, y) \mid x - y < 2\} = R_3 \cap R_4$.

$R_3 \cap R_4$ is graphed in Figure 104.

3. Let $R_5 = \{(x, y) \mid x^2 + y^2 = 2\}$, and
$R_6 = \{(x, y) \mid y = x^2\}$.

The graph of R_5 is a circle with radius equal to $\sqrt{2}$, whereas R_6 is a parabola. The solution for this system of equations is indicated in Figure 105.

$$\{(x, y) \mid x^2 + y^2 = 2 \quad and \quad y = x^2\} =$$
$$\{(x, y) \mid x^2 + y^2 = 2\} \cap \{(x, y) \mid y = x^2\} = R_5 \cap R_6.$$

122 ✳

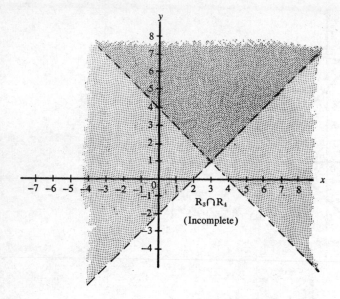

$R_3 \cap R_4$

(Incomplete)

Fig. 104

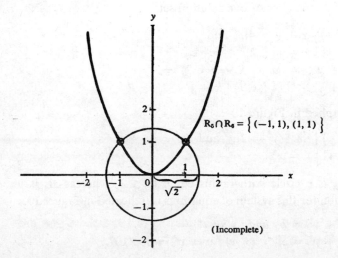

$R_5 \cap R_6 = \left\{ (-1, 1), (1, 1) \right\}$

$\sqrt{2}$

(Incomplete)

Fig. 105

RELATIONS AS UNION OF FUNCTIONS

Now let us consider a couple of examples of the operation of forming the union. In doing so, we shall also show that certain relations are simply a union of functions. Therefore we shall use examples in which the relations are functions. In both examples, the universe is $D \times D$.

1. Let $F_1 = \{(x, y) \mid y = \sqrt{4 - x^2}\}$, and
   $F_2 = \{(x, y) \mid y = -\sqrt{4 - x^2}\}$.

The graphs of these two functions are shown in Figure 106.

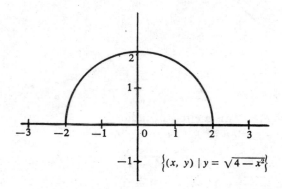

$$\{(x, y) \mid y = \sqrt{4 - x^2}\}$$

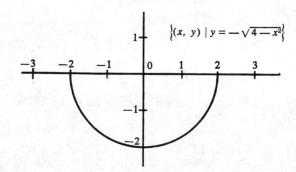

$$\{(x, y) \mid y = -\sqrt{4 - x^2}\}$$

Fig. 106

$$F_1 \cup F_2 = \{(x, y) \mid y = \sqrt{4 - x^2} \quad or \quad y = -\sqrt{4 - x^2}\},$$
$$= \{(x, y) \mid y = \sqrt{4 - x^2}\} \cup \{(x, y) \mid y = -\sqrt{4 - x^2}\}.$$

In other words, $F_1 \cup F_2$ is the set of ordered pairs satisfying the condition $y = \sqrt{4 - x^2}$ or $y = -\sqrt{4 - x^2}$. This includes all ordered pairs that are in F_1 or in F_2. The graph of $F_1 \cup F_2$ is shown in Figure 107.

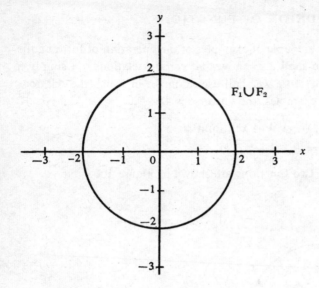

Fig. 107

Observe that the graph of $F_1 \cup F_2$ is a circle of radius 2.
We can develop the usual equation of $F_1 \cup F_2$ as follows:

$$y = \sqrt{4 - x^2} \quad or \quad y = -\sqrt{4 - x^2}.$$
$$\therefore \quad (y - \sqrt{4 - x^2})(y + \sqrt{4 - x^2}) = 0,$$
$$y^2 - (4 - x^2) = 0,$$
$$y^2 + x^2 = 4,$$
$$x^2 + y^2 = 4.$$

Thus

$$F_1 \cup F_2 = \{(x, y) \mid x^2 + y^2 = 4\} = \{(x, y) \mid y = \pm \sqrt{4 - x^2}\}.$$

This relation is obviously not a function, but we have shown that it is the union of functions, F_1 and F_2.

2. Now let $F_3 = \{(x, y) \mid y = \sqrt{x}\}$, and
$$F_4 = \{(x, y) \mid y = -\sqrt{x}\}.$$

The universe is $D \times D$. The graphs of these two functions are shown in Figure 108.

$$F_3 \cup F_4 = \{(x, y) \mid y = \sqrt{x} \quad or \quad y = -\sqrt{x}\},$$
$$= \{(x, y) \mid y = \sqrt{x}\} \cup \{(x, y) \mid y = -\sqrt{x}\}.$$

The graph of $F_3 \cup F_4$ is shown in Figure 109.
We observe that the graph of $F_3 \cup F_4$ is a parabola $(x = y^2)$.

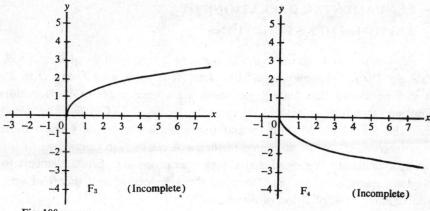

F₃ (Incomplete)

Fig. 108

F₄ (Incomplete)

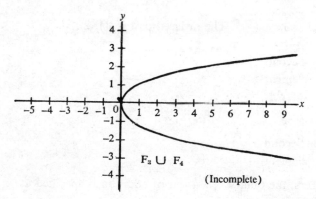

$F_3 \cup F_4$

(Incomplete)

Fig. 109

The usual equation of $F_3 \cup F_4$ is developed as follows:

$$y = \sqrt{x} \quad \text{or} \quad y = -\sqrt{x}.$$
$$\therefore \quad (y - \sqrt{x})(y + \sqrt{x}) = 0,$$
$$y^2 - x = 0,$$
$$x = y^2.$$

The relation $F_3 \cup F_4$ is not a function but the union of two functions, F_3 and F_4.

It should be observed that if we start with the relation, it can be broken up into the two functions.

FUNDAMENTAL OPERATIONS OF
ARITHMETIC AS FUNCTIONS

So far we have considered functions in a set such as $A \times A$, $A \times B$, $I \times I$, or $D \times D$, with mappings from A to A, A to B, I to I, and D to D. It can be shown that *binary* operations are special cases of the function concept; therefore we shall study them briefly here. In Chapter 2 we noted that the operations of addition and multiplication are binary operations. It is interesting now to go a step farther and relate such operations to the function concept. We recall that binary operations act on two elements to produce single elements, e.g., forming the intersection and union of sets, addition and multiplication of numbers.

Binary operations such as addition and multiplication may be defined as sets of ordered pairs where the first element is itself a pair of numbers. For example:

1. $(1, 2) \xrightarrow{+} 3$ The ordered pair is $[(1, 2), 3]$.

         ↑   ↑

         First   Second
         element   element

2. $(1, 2) \xrightarrow{\times} 2$ The ordered pair is $[(1, 2), 2]$.

         ↑   ↑

         First   Second
         element   element

Working with integers, the binary operation of addition is specified as

$$A = \{[(x, y), x + y] \mid (x, y) \in I \times I \text{ and } x + y \in I\}.$$

Some of the pairs of A would be

$$[(1, 2), 3], \ [(2, 2), 4], \ [(3, 2), 5], \ [(5, 4), 9].$$

We, of course, are used to using the following notation:

$$1 + 2 = 3, \quad 2 + 2 = 4, \quad 3 + 2 = 5, \quad 5 + 4 = 9.$$

The chief difference between these and other ordered pairs is that the first element of each ordered pair in a binary operation is itself an ordered pair. So we see that it is possible to consider functions from a Cartesian set such as $I \times I$ to I. In other words, we can map ordered pairs (x, y) of $I \times I$ onto individual members of I.

The domain of such a function F is a subset of $I \times I$ and the range is a subset of I. For addition of integers, the domain is $I \times I$ and the range is I.

We have observed that a function from A to B maps a member of A onto a member of B, each member of A having at most one image in B.

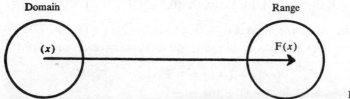

Fig. 110

In a binary operation, an ordered pair (x, y) maps onto z, or we say that z is the image of (x, y). The domain for such a function is the set of ordered pairs (x, y), whereas a member of the set of ordered pairs in the function is $[(x, y), z]$. To generalize, a binary operation on a set G is a function whose domain is a subset of $G \times G$ and whose range is a subset of G.

We have indicated that the simplest and most common examples of this type of function are the operations of addition and multiplication. Let us consider some specific examples wherein such functions map pairs of numbers onto single numbers.

1. The Binary Operation of Addition

Let the universe be a proper subset of $I \times I$ and let F be such that

$$F(x, y) = x + y.$$

The mapping of this function is expressed in Figure 111.

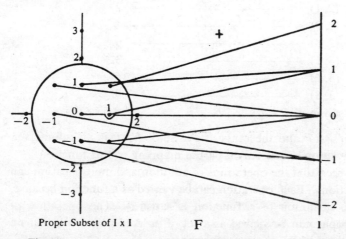

Fig. 111

To be more explicit, let us tabulate the set of ordered pairs in the domain as restricted in this example.

$$\{(-1, -1), (-1, 0), (-1, 1), (0, 1), (0, 0), (0, -1), (1, 1), (1, 0), (1, -1)\}$$

Therefore the sums (or images) of (x, y) are (-2), (-1), (0), (1), (0), (-1), (2), (1), (0) respectively; or in the traditional manner we can write:

$$(-1) + (-1) = -2$$
$$(-1) + (0) = -1$$
$$(-1) + (1) = 0$$
$$(0) + (1) = 1$$
$$(0) + (0) = 0$$
$$(0) + (-1) = -1$$
$$(1) + (1) = 2$$
$$(1) + (0) = 1$$
$$(1) + (-1) = 0$$

Note that nine elements of the domain map onto five elements of the range.

2. The Binary Operation of Multiplication

Let P be the positive integers and let F be such that $F(x, y) = x \cdot y$. A partial mapping of this function is expressed below.

$$\times$$

(1, 1)	1
(1, 2)	2
(1, 3)	3
(2, 1)	2
(2, 2)	4
(2, 3)	6
(3, 1)	3
(3, 2)	6
(3, 3)	9

Proper subset of $P \times P$ F P

The domain is $P \times P$ and the range is P. Since $P \times P$ is an infinite set, the preceding tabulation shows only a partial mapping of this function.

Now we have seen that the operations of addition and multiplication can be viewed as functions. Each operation can be viewed as a function because, in each case, the definition of a function is satisfied. The operation of addition, for example, can be viewed as a set of ordered pairs such that no two members of the set have the same first component.

ELEMENTARY FUNCTIONS AND THEIR PROPERTIES

Functions may be studied from the standpoint of the properties they exhibit. The following types of functions are those commonly presented in the secondary school.

1. The Linear Function

The linear function is defined by the general formula

$$y = mx + b,$$

where m, x, and b are elements of D. When we make replacements for m and b from D, we get a condition whose graph is a straight line that is a geometric picture of the set of pairs (x, y) that satisfy the condition. For this reason, we say that the general formula $y = mx + b$ defines a linear function. For each pair of replacements for m and b, we obtain a set of number pairs whose graph is a line. Corresponding to the set of all choices for m and b, we have a set of straight lines. Observe that m and b play the rôle of a variable in a special way. In situations such as this, we refer to m and b as parameters.

Let us consider a specific condition such as

$$y = 2x + 3.$$
$$\text{Let } F = \{(x, y) \mid y = 2x + 3\},$$
$$\text{then } F(x) = 2x + 3.$$

Now we may tabulate some ordered pairs and draw the graph for this function.

$$\text{If } Fx = 2x + 3,$$
$$\text{then } F(-2) = -1,$$
$$F(-1) = 1,$$
$$F(0) = 3,$$
$$F(1) = 5, \text{ and}$$
$$F(2) = 7.$$

Hence, we have the following table of values:

x	-2	-1	0	1	2
$F(x)$ or y	-1	1	3	5	7

The graph is shown in Figure 112.

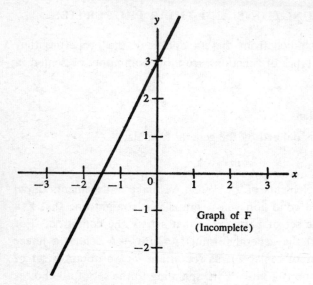

Graph of F
(Incomplete)

Fig. 112

The y-coordinate of the point at which the graph crosses the y-axis is known as the y-intercept. At this point, the first element of the number pair is zero, since $x = 0$ at all points on the y-axis. Therefore, the number pair containing the y-intercept will be $(0, y)$ which in this case is $(0, 3)$, since if $x = 0$, $2x + 3 = 2(0) + 3 = 3$. Hence, the y-intercept is 3. Similarly, the x-intercept can be determined by finding x in the number pair $(x, 0)$. For the graph of $y = 2x + 3$, it is $-\frac{3}{2}$.

For the general formula, $y = mx + b$, the y-intercept is b, since if $x = 0$, $mx = 0$, and therefore $y = b$. Similarly, we can show that the x-intercept for the general formula, $y = mx + b$, is $\dfrac{-b}{m}$, provided $m \neq 0$.

2. The Quadratic Function

The quadratic function is defined by the equation $y = ax^2 + bx + c$, where a, b, c, and x are all elements of D, and a, b, and c are regarded as parameters.

Suppose we have an equation such as

$$y = 2x^2 - 3x + 1.$$
$$\text{Let } F = \{(x, y) \mid y = 2x^2 - 3x + 1\},$$
$$\text{then } F(x) = 2x^2 - 3x + 1.$$

Using this last statement we can build the following table of values:

x	-2	-1	0	1	2	3
$F(x)$ or y	15	6	1	0	3	10

The graph of this function is shown in Figure 113.

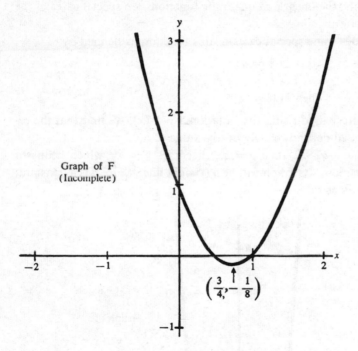

Graph of F
(Incomplete)

$\left(\dfrac{3}{4}, -\dfrac{1}{8}\right)$

Fig. 113

This function is the set of pairs $\{(x, ax^2 + bx + c)\}$. To find an x-intercept, we shall have to find a replacement for x in the number pair $(x, 0)$ such that $(x, 0)$ belongs to the function. If we let $ax^2 + bx + c = 0$, the value of x will be

$$\left(\frac{-b + \sqrt{b^2 - 4ac}}{2a}\right) \quad \text{or} \quad \left(\frac{-b - \sqrt{b^2 - 4ac}}{2a}\right)$$

provided $b^2 - 4ac \geq 0$. If $b^2 - 4ac = 0$ there will be just one x-intercept, and if $b^2 - 4ac < 0$ there will be no x-intercepts.

The zeros of a function are those values of x that make $F(x) = 0$. Thus we observe that the zeros of a quadratic function are in fact the solutions to the quadratic equation $F(x) = 0$.

3. The Polynomial Function

The general polynomial function is defined by

$$y = a_n x^n + a_{n-1} x^{n-1} + \ldots a_1 x^1 + a_0$$

where n is a non-negative integer and all coefficients are rational.

We shall not attempt to study this function in detail as it is rather complicated. Actually, the linear and quadratic functions are special cases of the polynomial function.

Let us consider some special cases of this function as defined by

$$y = ax^n.$$
$$\text{Let } F = \{(x, y) \mid y = ax^n\},$$
$$\text{then } F(x) = ax^n.$$

If numbers are paired using the notation $y = F(x)$, we find that the relationship expressed depends chiefly on the value of n.

(a) If $n = 1$ and $a > 0$, then $y = ax^n$ becomes $y = ax$, which defines a special linear function. Its graph will be a straight line. Since a is a constant, y will vary directly as x.

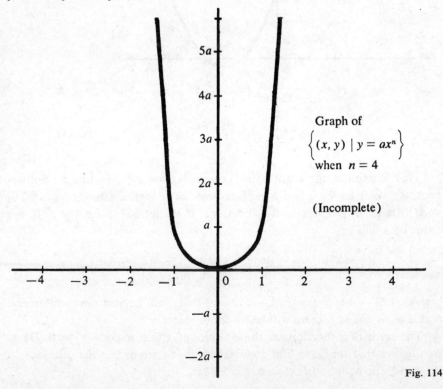

Graph of
$$\left\{(x, y) \mid y = ax^n\right\}$$
when $n = 4$

(Incomplete)

Fig. 114

(b) If n is an even positive integer and $a > 0$, the graph of $y = ax^n$ will be of the type or have the general shape of that shown in Figure 114.

If $n = 2$, y varies as x^2; if $n = 4$, y varies as x^4.

(c) If n is an odd positive integer and $a > 0$, the graph will be of the type or have the general shape of that shown in Figure 115.

If $n = 3$, y varies as x^3, if $n = 5$, y varies as x^5.

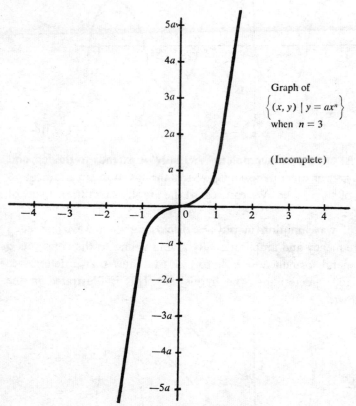

Graph of
$$\{(x, y) \mid y = ax^n\}$$
when $n = 3$

(Incomplete)

Fig. 115

4. The Trigonometric Functions

There are six widely used trigonometric functions: sine, cosine, tangent, cotangent, secant, cosecant. We shall consider only the sine function that is defined by the equation

$$y = a \sin bx.$$
$$\text{Let } F = \{(x, y) \mid y = a \sin bx\},$$
$$\text{then } F(x) = a \sin bx.$$

If we consider the simple formula, $y = \sin x$, we can use a set of tables to find $\sin x$ for the ordered pairs (x, y) or $(x, \sin x)$. The familiar sine curve is shown in Figure 116.

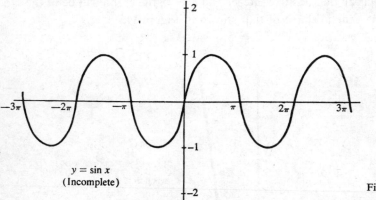

$y = \sin x$
(Incomplete)

Fig. 116

This graph is, of course, incomplete. Actually, it extends to the left and right indefinitely. For obvious reasons, we say the function is periodic, and that the period of $\sin x$ is 2π. We can regard the graph as picturing a sort of wave motion.

The study of wave motion in physics discloses that a wave has such properties as frequency and amplitude. By giving values to the constants a and b in the general formula $y = a \sin bx$, we can show that a determines the amplitude and b determines the frequency. This is illustrated in the graphs that follow:

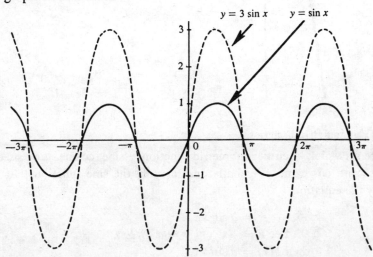

$y = 3 \sin x$ $y = \sin x$

Fig. 117

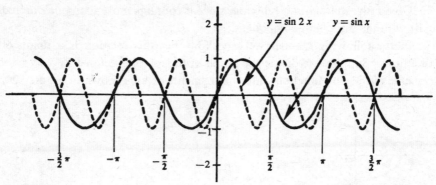

Fig. 118

It will be noted that the graph of the function defined by $y = 3 \sin x$, Figure 117, has three times the amplitude of the graph of the function defined by $y = \sin x$, and also that the graph of the function as defined by $y = \sin 2x$, Figure 118, has twice as many waves in the domain $-2\pi \leq x \leq 2\pi$ as does the graph of the function defined by $y = \sin x$ over the same domain. Therefore, the constants a and b in the general formula $y = a \sin bx$ have the significance indicated above.

The inverse of the sine function is defined by $x = \sin y$ (x and y interchanged in the original formula).

The graph of the inverse of the sine function is shown below:

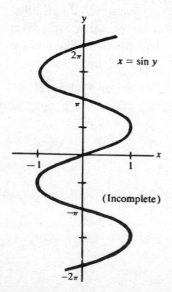

Fig. 119

Obviously, this is not a function, since it contains more than one ordered pair with the same first component.

In the following manner we can show that this relation is a union of functions. Suppose we divide the graph of the relation defined by $x = \sin y$ (inverse of the sine function) into the segments or arcs shown in Figure 120.

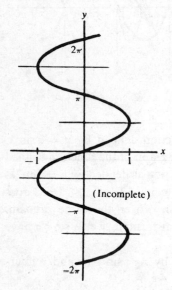

(Incomplete)

Fig. 120

Each of the arcs so indicated is the graph of a relation that is a function, since for each x there is at most one y such that (x, y) belongs to the relation. In this way, we create a new function and we also invent a new symbolism for it ($y = \arcsin x$). This function is useful in mathematics. The domain of this function is $\{x \mid -1 \leq x \leq 1\}$ and the range of this function is $\left\{ y \mid -\dfrac{\pi}{2} \leq y \leq \dfrac{\pi}{2} \right\}$. The graph of this function is shown on Figure 121.

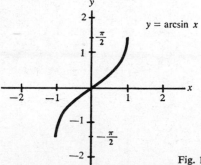

$y = \arcsin x$

Fig. 121

5. The Exponential and Logarithmic Functions

There are interesting conditions in two variables, in which one of the variables is an exponent. For example,

$$y = a^x \quad (a > 0 \text{ and } a \neq 1).$$

The variable x is the exponent of the power of a that equals y; x is also known as the logarithm of y. It is important to remember that a logarithm is an exponent. When we write $2^4 = 16$, we are using exponential notation; when we write $\log_2 16 = 4$, we are using logarithmic notation. In each case the logarithm is 4.

The exponential function may be defined as follows:

$$F = \{(x, y) \mid y = a^x\},$$
$$= \{(x, y) \mid x = \log_a y\}.$$

The inverse of this function, the logarithmic function, is defined as follows:

$$F^i = \{(x, y) \mid x = a^y\},$$
$$= \{(x, y) \mid y = \log_a x\}.$$

By setting up tables of values for the ordered pairs in these two functions (x, a^x) or $(x, \log_a x)$, we can construct their graphs as shown in Figure 122.

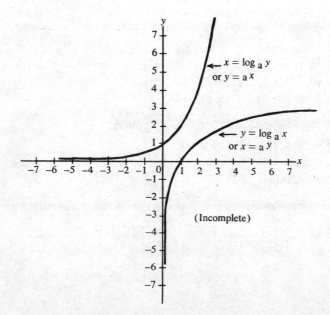

Fig. 122

PROBLEMS FOR REVIEW

1. For each of the following, indicate whether or not the relation is a function:

(a)

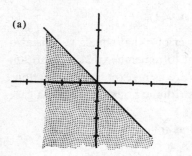

(b)

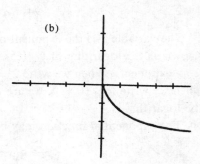

(c)

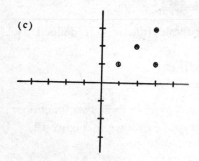

(d)

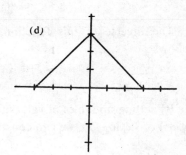

2. For each of the relations given below, indicate whether or not the relation is a function.

   (a) $R = \{(1, 2), (2, 2), (4, 3), (1, 3), (3, 3)\}$.

   (b) $R = \{(a, a), (b, d), (c, e), (f, g), (g, h)\}$.

   (c) $R = \{(3, 4), (4, 5), (5, 6), (4, 7), (7, 8)\}$.

3. Which of the following relations are functions? Explain.

   (a) $R = \{(x, y) \mid y^2 = x + 1\}$. $(U = I \times I)$

   (b) $R = \{(x, y) \mid y < x\}$. $(U = N \times N)$

   (c) $R = \{(x, y) \mid y$ is the father of $x\}$.

4. For each of the following conditions, select those that define a function.

   (a) $x^2 - 3 = -y^2$.

   (b) $y = 4x$.

   (c) $x = y^2$.

   (d) $y = \dfrac{1}{x}$.

5. Consider the following functions in $D \times D$.

(a) $F = \{(x, y) \mid y = x - 1\}$.
(b) $G = \{(x, y) \mid y = x^2 - 1\}$.
(c) $H = \{(x, y) \mid y = 3x + 4\}$.

Calculate the following for the preceding functions:

$$F(1), \quad F(-2), \quad F(4), \quad F(0),$$
$$G(1), \quad G(-2), \quad G(4), \quad G(0),$$
$$H(1), \quad H(-2), \quad H(4), \quad H(0).$$

6. Suppose we have the following function in $D \times D$:

$$F = \{(x, y) \mid y = 2\}.$$

(a) What are the domain and range of this function?
(b) Describe F as a mapping.

7. Let the function F in $D \times D$ be:

$$F = \{(x, y) \mid y = x + 2\}.$$

(a) What is the inverse of this function?
(b) Is F a one-to-one function? Explain fully.
(c) What are the domains and ranges of F and F^i?

8. Consider the following two functions in $D \times D$:

$$F_1 = \{(x, y) \mid x + y = 8\}.$$
$$F_2 = \{(x, y) \mid x - y = 4\}.$$

(a) Find the solution set of $\{x + y = 8 \text{ and } x - y = 4\}$ through the operation of intersection.
(b) Graph $F_1 \cap F_2$.

9. (a) Graph $\{(x, y) \mid x + y = 4\} \cup \{(x, y) \mid y = 2\}$ in $D \times D$.
(b) How would you describe this union?

10. Graph $\{(x, y) \mid y < -2\} \cup \{(x, y) \mid x < -2\}$ in $D \times D$.

11. Explain what is meant by saying that a relation may be a union of functions.

BIBLIOGRAPHY

1. ALLENDOERFER, C. B. and OAKLEY, C. O: *Principles of Mathematics*. New York: McGraw-Hill Book Company, 1952.

2. *Sets, Relations, and Functions*. Commission on Mathematics of the College Entrance Examination Board, 1958.

3. *Functions and Operations Deductive Theories*. Mathematics Staff of the College. University of Chicago, 1956.

4. *Insights into Modern Mathematics*. 23rd Yearbook: National Council of Teachers of Mathematics, 1957. NCTM, Washington, D.C.

5. *The Growth of Mathematical Ideas, Grades K—12*. 24th Yearbook: National Council of Teachers of Mathematics, 1959. NCTM. Washington, D.C.

7 ELEMENTARY LOGIC AND PROOF

The preceding chapters have a definite sequential arrangement, inasmuch as ideas emerging from each are developed to form the content of succeeding chapters. This chapter will help to clarify some of the concepts presented thus far. It will also give some necessary background for the discussion of mathematical systems in Chapter 8. We shall consider only the most fundamental ideas of logic. The material included in this chapter is by no means complete. It is simply an introduction and orientation to a very elementary part of symbolic logic.

Logic has been an area of study for well over two thousand years. Before the birth of Christ, such prominent men as Socrates, Aristotle, and Plato were outstanding scholars in the art of logic. Socrates tried to establish a "universal" definition of such words as *justice* and *right*; that is, he sought definitions which would be true under all conditions. He is also credited with the creation of the *dialectical argument* which is basically the question-and-answer technique. The books on logic written by Aristotle were studied intensively for centuries after they were written, especially during the period of Scholasticism. For the popular course in dialectics in the days of the early Roman Empire the chief references were these books of logic by Aristotle.

There were several reasons for the intensive study of logic during the Middle Ages. After the advent of Christianity, many felt that the position of the church would be strengthened if its beliefs could be proved by reason (logic) as well as accepted by faith. Logic provided the means (forms) by which man could think in an orderly fashion. It was assumed that any argument could be reduced to a standardized form and that, if one went through certain sequential steps without error, he would arrive at a correct answer.

In this chapter we shall focus our attention upon *symbolic* logic, which subjects logic to the symbols and procedures of mathematics. In doing this, we shall: (1) discuss that part of symbolic logic that deals with connectives and statements, (2) develop a formal method of determining the logical truth or falsity of compound statements by means of truth-tables, and (3) indicate the relationship of symbolic logic to mathematical proof.

CONNECTIVES AND COMPOUND STATEMENTS

In an earlier chapter we discussed compound statements and noted that certain connectives were used in combining simple statements to form compound statements. For example, we considered statements and conditions such as those expressed below:

1. John is a policeman *and* John is Irish.
2. Tom is a track star *or* Tom is a football player.
3. $x + y \geq 4$.

The connectives are *and* and *or*. There are other connectives that are frequently used in mathematics to establish the structure and give precise meaning to mathematical sentences. In addition to *and* and *or*, we shall consider the following three connectives: *not*; *if* . . ., *then* . . .; and *if and only if* . . .. For example:

1. The house is *not* white.
2. *If* Mary plays the piano, *then* Jane will sing.
3. John will weed the garden *if and only if* Bob will wash the car.

NOTE. Although *not* modifies a single statement and does not connect two statements, it is common practice in mathematics to call it a connective.

In this chapter we will be concerned with how the truth value of a compound statement is determined from the truth values of the simple statements that make up the compound statement. We are interested in the ideas expressed and not in the words used to express these ideas.

We shall refer to the simple statements as the components of compound statements. When writing compound sentences in symbolic form, we shall use small letters such as p, q, r, etc. The connectives may be represented by symbols. The following are usually accepted and used by mathematicians:

$\sim$ for *not*

$\wedge$ for *and*

$\vee$ for *or*

$\rightarrow$ for *if* . . ., *then* . . .,

$\leftrightarrow$ for *if and only if*

With the foregoing symbols, we can write the following compound sentences:

$$\sim p$$
$$p \wedge q$$
$$p \vee q$$
$$p \rightarrow q$$
$$p \leftrightarrow q$$

If we replace p by "Mary will play the piano", and q by "Jane will sing", we obtain the statements expressed below:

Mary will *not* play the piano.
Mary will play the piano *and* Jane will sing.
Mary will play the piano *or* Jane will sing.
If Mary will play the piano, *then* Jane will sing.
Mary will play the piano, *if and only if* Jane will sing.

Compound statements are given specific names, depending on the connective used. The following table gives the five connectives in words and in symbols, and the names of the corresponding compound statements.

Connective	*Compound Statement*
not ($\sim$)	negation
and ($\wedge$)	conjunction
or ($\vee$)	disjunction
if . . ., then . . . ($\rightarrow$)	conditional
if and only if ($\leftrightarrow$)	biconditional

The connectives used in elementary logic are commonly called *logical connectives*. Each connective is a very important part of a compound statement, because the truth-value of a compound statement depends not only on the truth-value of its components but also on the meaning we give to the logical connectives.

TRUTH-TABLES FOR THE LOGICAL CONNECTIVES

We shall agree that every statement has truth-value associated with it, *truth* for true statements and *falsity* for false statements. We shall symbolize truth by T and falsity by F. We shall first consider the truth-values of compound statements which contain only one logical connective.

Negation

To indicate the negation of a statement, we may prefix it with the phrase "It is false that", or use the connective *not*. For example, the negation of "Mary will play the piano" would be "It is false that Mary will play the piano" or "Mary will not play the piano". If we use the variable p, and think of its domain as the set of all possible statements, then for the generalization of the negation of p, we write $\sim p$, which is read "not p".

A statement and its negation have opposite truth values. That is, if p is true, $\sim p$ is false; if p is false, $\sim p$ is true. The truth-table for the negation is as follows:

When p is	$\sim p$ is
T	F
F	T

It should be pointed out that, in logic, we must use the qualifiers "not" or "it is false that" to get a negation. "It is black" is not the negation of "It is white." "It is cold" is not the negation of "It is warm". If something is not white it is not necessarily black, and if something is not warm it is not necessarily cold. The correct negations would be: "It is not white" or "It is false that it is white," and "It is not warm" or "It is false that it is warm".

Conjunction

In a conjunction, two statements are combined by the use of the connective *and*. Given the simple statements

> p: The roads are good.
> q: We shall drive to town.

we obtain from $p \wedge q$ the conjunction,

> The roads are good *and* we shall drive to town.

Since we have two variables, there are four possible combinations: (1) both p and q are true, (2) p is true and q is false, (3) p is false and q is true,

(4) both p and q are false. The domain of the variables is the set of all possible statements. The four generalizations for all replacements of p and q are given by the following truth-table:

p	q	$p \wedge q$
T	T	T
T	F	F
F	T	F
F	F	F

This table confirms what we learned in an earlier chapter, that a compound statement involving the connective *and* is true just when both of its components are true, and false when either one or both of its components are false.

Disjunction

In a disjunction, we combine two given statements by means of the connective *or*. For example, from $p \vee q$ we obtain the disjunction,

Mary will play the piano *or* Jane will sing.

In ordinary discourse, the connective *or* is used in two different ways. That is, *or* may have one of two meanings. Used inclusively, it refers to one or the other or to both. Used exclusively, it refers to one or the other but not to both. In mathematics, the inclusive meaning is preferred. This is sometimes referred to as the "and/or" interpretation. For example, if we say "John is a hockey player or John is a tennis player", we mean that John is either a hockey player or a tennis player or both. He must be at least one of "a hockey player" or "a tennis player" if the compound statement is to be true. Therefore we can conclude that a disjunction ($p \vee q$) can be false only if both components (p, q) are false. The truth-table for the disjunction is as follows:

p	q	$p \vee q$
T	T	T
T	F	T
F	T	T
F	F	F

In reading about compound statements such as negation, conjunction, and disjunction, it is quite possible to sense the similarity between them and certain operations discussed in an earlier chapter. In our discussion of operations on sets, we noted that two of them were operations on two sets to produce one new set. These operations were called forming the union and forming the intersection. Furthermore, we observed that the operation of forming the intersection was related to the connective *and*, and the operation of forming the union was related to the connective *or*. There is also a similarity between the operation of forming the complement for sets and negation of a statement in logic. The complement of set A is $\sim A$ (or $\bar{A}$) meaning "not A", and in logic the negation of p is $\sim p$, meaning "not p".

In the chapter on sets, we used Venn diagrams to illustrate the operations of intersection, union, and complementation. Now let us illustrate the relationship between sets and the compound statements of conjunction, disjunction, and negation by the use of Venn diagrams.

Let p and q be statements and let U be their set of logical possibilities. Let P and Q be the subsets of the universe for which statements p and q are respectively true. In mathematics, the sets P and Q are known as truth sets.

We have observed that the compound statement $p \wedge q$ is true only when p is true and q is true. But the intersection of P and Q, which is written $P \cap Q$, is the set consisting of the logical possibility p true and q true. Hence $P \cap Q$ is the truth set of $p \wedge q$.

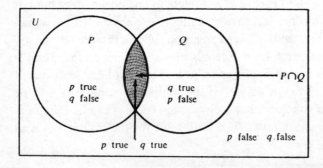

Fig. 123

Using the same conditions, we can show that the truth set for $p \vee q$ is the union of P and Q.

$P \cup Q$ is the truth set of $p \vee q$, since $p \vee q$ is false only when both p and q are false, and true in the three other cases.

Elementary logic and proof

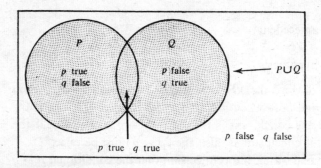

Fig. 124

Let *P* be the set of logical possibilities for which the statement *p* is true. It follows then that since ∼*P* is true and *P* is false, the truth set of ∼*P* contains all logical possibilities for which *P* is false. That is, the truth set of ∼*P* is *P̄*. This set is shaded in Figure 125.

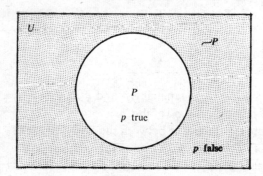

Fig. 125

Conditional

Compound statements of the *if . . ., then . . .* form, which are known as conditionals, are frequently used in mathematics. We shall consider them in quite some detail. We have said that the conditional is expressed as follows:

$$p \rightarrow q.$$

This is read "if *p*, then *q*".

We shall learn that $p \rightarrow q$ and $q \rightarrow p$ do not always have the same truth-value. Since the order of appearance of the components in a conditional is important, we call the first component *p* the antecedent or hypothesis and the second component *q* the consequent or conclusion.

$$p \xrightarrow{\hspace{3cm}} q$$

antecedent	consequent
or	or
hypothesis	conclusion

It should be fairly obvious that the conditional $p \to q$ will be true when both p and q are true and false when p is true and q is false. That is, if the hypothesis is true and the conclusion is true, then $p \to q$ is true, but if the hypothesis is true and the conclusion is false, then $p \to q$ must be false.

When p is false, we make an arbitrary decision that the conditional $p \to q$ is always true. However, this arbitrary decision is reasonable since we should realize that it is possible to get a true conclusion from a false hypothesis and that one might readily get a false conclusion from a false hypothesis.

It follows that the truth-table for $p \to q$ is as follows:

p	q	$p \to q$
T	T	T
T	F	F
F	T	T
F	F	T

Any compound statement resulting from replacing p and q in $p \to q$ by simple statements is false only if p is true and q is false.

Finally, let us observe that there is a difference between the ordinary use of *if . . ., then . . .* and the use of *if . . ., then . . .* in mathematical logic. In ordinary use there is some causal connection between the antecedent and the consequent. In mathematical use, there need not be causal connection between the antecedent and the consequent. Let us cite an example.

Suppose the following simple statements are used as replacements for the variables p and q:

> p: John is twelve years old.
> q: December 25 is Christmas Day.

Assuming that p is true and q is true, we can say that in the logic of mathematics, it is true that

1. *If* John is 12 years old, *then* December 25 is Christmas Day.
2. *If* John is *not* 12 years old, *then* December 25 is Christmas Day.
3. *If* John is *not* 12 years old, *then* December 25 is *not* Christmas Day.

These three conditionals are true, since a conditional is false only when the antecedent is true and the consequent is false.

Biconditional

We have noted that the biconditional is usually written as follows:

$$p \leftrightarrow q.$$

The symbol $\leftrightarrow$ suggests a combination of the symbols $(\rightarrow)$ and $(\leftarrow)$. So, from $p \leftrightarrow q$ we get the statement

$$(p \rightarrow q) \wedge (q \rightarrow p).$$

In the statement above, $p \rightarrow q$ and $q \rightarrow p$ may be regarded as components although each is a compound statement. Analysing the statement in this manner, we actually have a conjunction and we call $\wedge$ the *principal connective*.

It follows that $p \leftrightarrow q$ will be true if and only if both $p \rightarrow q$ and $q \rightarrow p$ are true. Consequently, to help get the truth-table for the biconditional, we shall use the truth-table for $(p \rightarrow q) \wedge (q \rightarrow p)$.

p	q	$p \rightarrow q$	$q \rightarrow p$	$(p \rightarrow q) \wedge (q \rightarrow p)$
T	T	T	T	T
T	F	F	T	F
F	T	T	F	F
F	F	T	T	T

We are familiar with the first four columns of this table. Although the last column is new to us, it should not be difficult to follow if we refer to the truth-table for the conjunction.

From the last column of the preceding table, we observe that

$$(p \rightarrow q) \wedge (q \rightarrow p)$$

is true, just in case both p and q are true or both p and q are false. Therefore, the truth-table for the biconditional is as follows:

p	q	$p \leftrightarrow q$
T	T	T
T	F	F
F	T	F
F	F	T

A biconditional is true if and only if its components have the same truth-value, and false if its components have opposite truth-values. In other words, a biconditional is true *if and only if* its components are both true or both false. In such instances, the phrase *if and only if* has real significance and it is important to use it where biconditionals are involved.

The following are two examples of the biconditional:

1. Jane loves Bob *if and only if* she accepts his invitation. $(p \leftrightarrow q)$

This could be written as follows:

> *If* Jane loves Bob, *then* she accepts his invitation; *and if* Jane accepts his invitation, *then* she loves Bob. $(p \rightarrow q) \wedge (q \rightarrow p)$

2. $2x + 1 = 7$, *if and only if* $x = 3$. $(p \leftrightarrow q)$

This could be written:

> *If* $2x + 1 = 7$, *then* $x = 3$; and *if* $x = 3$, *then* $2x + 1 = 7$.
> $$(p \rightarrow q) \wedge (q \rightarrow p)$$

With respect to the five basic truth-tables (negation, conjunction, disjunction, conditional, and biconditional), it should be thoroughly understood that they can be used quite apart from any specific components. The tables are generalizations for the variables p and q, whose domain is the set of all possible statements.

OTHER CONDITIONALS ASSOCIATED WITH A GIVEN CONDITIONAL

Three other conditionals, known as the converse, inverse, and contrapositive, are closely associated with each conditional $(p \rightarrow q)$.

Given the conditional: *If p, then q.* $(p \rightarrow q)$

1. Converse: *If q, then p.* $(q \rightarrow p)$
2. Inverse: *If not p, then not q.* $(\sim p \rightarrow \sim q)$
3. Contrapositive: *If not q, then not p.* $(\sim q \rightarrow \sim p)$

If the conditional is true, its converse or its inverse is not necessarily true. However, the conditional $(p \rightarrow q)$ and its contrapositive $(\sim p \rightarrow \sim q)$ always have the same truth-value.

Let us review this by citing examples:

1. The converse of a true conditional is not always true.

    (a) $p \rightarrow q$: *If* ABCD is a square,
              then ABCD is a rectangle. (True)
    (b) $q \rightarrow p$: *If* ABCD is a rectangle,
              then ABCD is a square. (False)

We can generalize this case with truth-tables. Since we are concerned with the converse of a true conditional, we shall use only the combinations of p and q that make $p \rightarrow q$ true. Then we shall construct the corresponding table for $q \rightarrow p$:

p	q	$p \rightarrow q$
T	T	T
F	T	T ◄
F	F	T

p	q	$q \rightarrow p$
T	T	T
F	T	F ◄
F	F	T

Observe that the truth values of $p \rightarrow q$ and $q \rightarrow p$ are not always the same. Hence, if a conditional is true, we cannot conclude that its converse is true.

2. The inverse of a true conditional is not always true.

    (a) $p \rightarrow q$:   *If* ABCD is a square,
                  then ABCD is a rectangle. (True)
    (b) $\sim p \rightarrow \sim q$: *If* ABCD is *not* a square,
                  then ABCD is *not* a rectangle. (False)

We can generalize with truth-tables as follows:

p	q	$p \rightarrow q$
T	T	T
F	T	T ◄
F	F	T

p	q	$\sim p$	$\sim q$	$\sim p \rightarrow \sim q$
T	T	F	F	T
F	T	T	F	F ◄
F	F	T	T	T

Hence, if a conditional is true, we cannot conclude that its inverse is true.

3. The conditional and its contrapositive always have the same truth-value.

(a) $p \to q$:　　*If* ABCD is a square,
　　　　　　　　then ABCD is a rectangle. (True)
(b) $\sim q \to \sim p$:　*If* ABCD is *not* a rectangle,
　　　　　　　　then ABCD is *not* a square. (True)

Let us again generalize with truth-tables.

p	q	$p \to q$	p	q	$\sim q$	$\sim p$	$\sim q \to \sim p$
T	T	T	T	T	F	F	T
T	F	F	T	F	T	F	F
F	T	T	F	T	F	T	T
F	F	T	F	F	T	T	T

From these, we observe that the conditional $(p \to q)$ and its contrapositive $(\sim q \to \sim p)$ are both true or both false for corresponding logical possibilities of p and q. In particular, we note that whenever $p \to q$ is true, $\sim q \to \sim p$ is also true.

ANALYSIS OF MORE COMPLICATED COMPOUND
STATEMENTS FOR TRUTH-VALUE

We shall now consider the truth-value of compound (or composite) statements that are more complicated than the statements we have been discussing. For example, suppose we have the statement:

If the roads are good, then we shall drive to town; and John will buy an elephant.

We can express the original statement in symbolic form as follows:

$$(p \to q) \wedge r.$$

Now let us assume the following truth-values for p, q, and r:

p:　The roads are good　　(assumed truth-value: T)
q:　We shall drive to town　　(assumed truth-value: T)
r:　John will buy an elephant　(assumed truth-value: F)

The truth-value of complicated compound statements can be determined through applications of the five simple truth-tables we have discussed. Therefore, when considering the truth-values of such compound statements, we are well advised to keep the five basic tables before us. To simplify matters, we can make one basic table which contains all the data of the five tables.

p	*q*	∼*p*	*p* ∧ *q*	*p* ∨ *q*	*p* → *q*	*p* ↔ *q*
T	T	F	T	T	T	T
T	F	F	F	T	F	F
F	T	T	F	T	T	F
F	F	T	F	F	T	T

Now let us return to our compound statement, $(p \rightarrow q) \wedge r$, and determine its truth-value. We shall first give our attention to the statement within the parentheses, which is $p \rightarrow q$. Since we have assumed that p and q are true, we know that $p \rightarrow q$ is true. The connective ∧ (*and*) is the principal connective. Now we have a conjunction between $p \rightarrow q$, which is true, and r, which is assumed false. Referring to our basic table, we observe that a conjunction of a true component and a false component is false. Therefore, the truth-value of $(p \rightarrow q) \wedge r$ is false when p and q are true and r is false.

Now suppose we have the statement expressed below:

$$(p \vee q) \rightarrow (\sim s \leftrightarrow t).$$

We can determine its truth-value if we know the truth-values of the components, simply by referring to our basic table. Since the principal connective is → (*if . . ., then . . .*), the whole statement is a conditional.

Let us assume that p and s are both true and that q and t are both false. First, let us consider the disjunction $p \vee q$. If p is true and q is false, then $p \vee q$ is true. Next, if s is true, $\sim s$ is false and since t is false, the biconditional $\sim s \leftrightarrow t$ is true. Finally, the truth-value of the whole statement is T (true), since a conditional is true when both the antecedent and consequent are true. All of this can be verified by checking each step with the basic table.

As one becomes accustomed to determining truth-values of complicated compound statements in this manner, it is possible and permissible to shorten the procedure by simply entering the names for truth-values below the name of each component and connective. Let us examine this method in some detail by analysing a specific statement such as $(p \vee q) \rightarrow (\sim s \leftrightarrow t)$ for one possible set of truth-values for p, q, s, t. Suppose the set of truth-values is as follows: p: T; q: F; s: T; t: F. With this knowledge, we can commence our analysis by writing the names of these truth-values under the names of the corresponding variables as follows:

$$(p \lor q) \to (\sim s \leftrightarrow t).$$
$$\text{T} \quad \text{F} \qquad \text{T} \quad \text{F}$$

Next, we enter the truth-values for each compound statement under the symbol for the appropriate connective, except the principal connective. For the first compound statement $(p \lor q)$, we enter the symbol T under the symbol $\lor$, since a disjunction is true (T) when p is true and q is false. In the compound statement $(\sim s \leftrightarrow t)$, we write the symbol F under the negation symbol since when s is true, $\sim s$ is false, and we write the symbol T under the biconditional symbol since $\sim s$ is false and t is false. After making these entries, our analysis is expressed as follows:

$$(p \lor q) \to (\sim s \leftrightarrow t).$$
$$\text{T T F} \qquad \text{FT T F}$$
$$\uparrow \qquad\qquad \uparrow$$
$$\text{true} \qquad\qquad \text{true}$$

Finally, under the symbol for the principal connective, we write the symbol T, since a conditional is true when the antecedent is true and the consequent is true. The final analysis in abbreviated form is expressed below:

$$(p \lor q) \to (\sim s \leftrightarrow t).$$
$$\text{T} \qquad \text{T} \qquad \text{T}$$
$$\uparrow$$
The statement is true.

For the analysis of succeeding compound statements, we shall use a shortened form rather than one of greater detail. The abbreviated form will serve our purpose quite adequately.

STATEMENT PATTERNS

A statement pattern is a condition for representing all statements having the same connective structure as the pattern.

Consider the following statements:

1. *If* it is raining, *then* it is *not* raining.
2. *If* John is a student, *then* John is *not* a student.
3. *If* $2 = 2$, *then* $2 \neq 2$.

Each statement expressed above has the same basic pattern. This pattern is symbolized by the following sentence:

$$p \rightarrow \sim p.$$

Since p is either true or false, we can make a truth-value table in the following manner:

$$
\begin{array}{ccc}
p & \rightarrow & \sim p \\
T & F & F \\
F & T & T
\end{array}
$$

Observe that any statement having the pattern $p \rightarrow \sim p$ is false if p is a true statement and true if p is a false statement. The foregoing table may be called the truth-table of the statement pattern $p \rightarrow \sim p$. Observe that there are only two lines in this table, since we have only one variable p, which is either true or false.

The statements we have studied in the earlier sections of this chapter, such as $p \wedge q$ and $p \vee q$, are also statement patterns when we think of p and q as variables whose domain is the set of all possible statements. We have observed that when we have two variables the complete truth-table has four lines.

Now suppose we are given the statement pattern expressed below:

$$(p \vee q) \rightarrow (p \wedge \sim q).$$

The following are instances of this statement pattern:

1. *If* Mary will play the piano *or* Jane will sing, *then* Mary will play the piano *and* Jane will *not* sing.
2. *If* $3 + 2 = 5$ *or* $3 + 4 = 7$, *then* $3 + 2 = 5$ *and* $3 + 4 \neq 7$.

Observe that we can obtain statement (1) from our pattern by replacing the variables p and q by the statements expressed below:

$$
\begin{aligned}
&p: \quad \text{Mary will play the piano.} \\
&q: \quad \text{Jane will sing.}
\end{aligned}
$$

First, $p \vee q$ yields: "Mary will play the piano *or* Jane will sing", and $p \wedge \sim q$ yields: "Mary will play the piano *and* Jane will *not* sing." Since the principal connective is $\rightarrow$, which is "*if* . . ., *then* . . .", the completed statement after all replacements is:

If Mary will play the piano *or* Jane will sing, *then* Mary will play the piano *and* Jane will *not* sing.

If we assume that (a) Mary will play the piano (p true) and (b) Jane will sing (q true), then the truth-value of statement (1) is expressed below:

$$(p \lor q) \to (p \land \sim q).$$
$$\text{T} \quad \text{F} \quad \text{F}$$
$$\uparrow$$

The statement is false.

By considering all possible combinations of truth-values or logical possibilities for p and q, we can derive the truth-table for this statement pattern as follows:

p	q	$p \lor q \to p \land \sim q$		
T	T	T	F	F
T	F	T	T	T
F	T	T	F	F
F	F	F	T	F

Finally, let us derive the truth-table for the pattern $p \land (q \to r)$, which has variables p, q, and r. With three variables, the table will have eight lines.

p	q	r	$p \land (q \to r)$		
T	T	T	T	T	T
T	F	T	T	T	T
F	T	T	F	F	T
F	F	T	F	F	T
T	T	F	T	F	F
T	F	F	T	F	T
F	T	F	F	F	F
F	F	F	F	F	T

One example or instance of this pattern, $p \land (q \to r)$, is:

Jean will dance, *and if* Mary will play the piano Jane will sing.

As you continue your study of statements and connectives, you will discover that there are many statement patterns, since certain statements have one connective structure, while other sets of statements have still other connective patterns.

Logical Validity

In the truth-tables of the preceding section, the truth-values of the composite statements were expressed in the column immediately below the symbol for the principal connective in each case. For each of the three examples, the various combinations of the variables yielded both true and false truth-values for the compound statement. There are some statement patterns that have no false instances. For example,

1. The disjunction, $p \vee \sim p$:

$$
\begin{array}{ccc}
p & \vee & \sim p \\
\mathbf{T} & \mathbf{T} & F \\
F & \mathbf{T} & T
\end{array}
$$

2. You will remember that we found $(p \rightarrow q) \leftrightarrow (\sim q \rightarrow \sim p)$ also does not yield any false instances.

p	q	$(p \rightarrow q)$	$\leftrightarrow$	$(\sim q \rightarrow \sim p)$
T	T	T	**T**	T
T	F	F	**T**	F
F	T	T	**T**	T
F	F	T	**T**	T

Statement patterns that have no false instances are known as *logically valid statement patterns*. Such patterns can be discovered by truth-table analysis. If a statement pattern is a logically valid statement pattern, the column under the symbol for the principal connective will contain only the symbol T.

It is useful to know which patterns are logically valid patterns, as they can be regarded as always true without question or justification. Patterns that have the conditional or biconditional as the principal connective are of particular importance in mathematics. Some other examples of logically valid patterns are expressed below:

1. CONDITIONALS: $[(p \rightarrow q) \wedge (q \rightarrow r)] \rightarrow (p \rightarrow r)$.
$\qquad\qquad\qquad\quad [p \wedge (p \rightarrow q)] \rightarrow q$.

2. BICONDITIONALS: $(p \rightarrow q) \leftrightarrow (\sim q \rightarrow \sim p)$.
$\qquad\qquad\qquad\quad (p \leftrightarrow q) \leftrightarrow [(p \rightarrow q) \wedge (q \rightarrow p)]$.

Logical Equivalence

In a logically valid biconditional, the two statements involved are said to be logically equivalent. Two composite statements are logically equivalent if the resulting truth-values of the two statements are the same for whatever truth-values are assigned to the initial components. For example, the two composite statements that are expressed below are logically equivalent as shown by their truth-table analysis.

p	q	$\sim(p \to q)$	,	$p \wedge \sim q$
T	T	F T		T F F
T	F	T F		T T T
F	T	F T		F F F
F	F	F T		F F F

Now if we determine the truth-values for the biconditional

$$\sim(p \to q) \leftrightarrow (p \wedge \sim q),$$

we shall find no false instances and, therefore, this biconditional is logically valid.

$$\sim(p \to q) \leftrightarrow (p \wedge \sim q)$$
F	T	F
T	T	T
F	T	F
F	T	F

Because of the foregoing analysis, we say that *logical equivalence is logical validity of the biconditional.*

Some other examples of logical equivalents are expressed below. Each may be tested by truth-tables in accordance with the preceding method.

$$\sim(\sim p) \quad , \quad p.$$
$$\sim(p \wedge q) \quad , \quad \sim p \vee \sim q.$$
$$(p \wedge q) \to r \quad , \quad p \to (q \to r).$$

Logical Implication

We often say that one statement follows logically from another statement or other statements. For example:

Elementary logic and proof

1. *From* Mary is happy or Mary is sad.
      Mary is not sad.
   To Mary is happy.
      $[(p \lor q) \land \sim q] \to p$.

2. *From* If Mary is happy, then Tom is sad.
      Tom is not sad.
   To Mary is not happy.
      $[(p \to q) \land \sim q] \to \sim p$.

Let us compute the truth-table for the first conditional using our shortened method. We shall, of course, think of p and q as variables, whose domain is the set of all possible statements.

p	q	$[(p \lor q) \land \sim q]$	$\to$	p
T	T	F	T	T
T	F	T	T	T
F	T	F	T	F
F	F	F	T	F

Since we find no false instances (all truth-values are T expressed under principal connective), we say that this conditional is logically valid. The truth-table for (2) may be computed in like manner.

Logical validity of the conditional is called logical implication. When conditionals are logical implications, we use the words "logically implies" or simply "implies" to express the principal connective $\to$. For example, we say that $(p \lor q) \land \sim q$ logically implies p, and $(p \to q) \land \sim q$ logically implies $\sim p$.

We have indicated on page 157 that the two conditions expressed below are logically valid:

$$[(p \to q) \land (q \to r)] \to (p \to r).$$
$$[p \land (p \to q)] \to q.$$

Since these conditionals are logically valid, we can say that

$$(p \to q) \land (q \to r) \text{ implies } (p \to r), \quad \text{and}$$
$$p \land (p \to q) \text{ implies } q.$$

INFERENCE AND PROOF

The preceding material is basic to certain aspects of contemporary mathematics. For example, there is a direct relationship between logic and proof. After a preliminary discussion of the elements of proof, we shall indicate briefly how logic is related to this section on inference and proof.

Everyone is interested in proof. This is evident from much of what we hear and read. Children are satisfied with arguments which have little or no validity but which serve at the time to justify their position. For example, we often hear children back up their arguments by such statements as: "Teacher said so", "My mother told me", "I saw it in the daily newspaper", "Everyone knows it is true."

We have said that children make such statements, but we know perfectly well that many adults also argue in a similar fashion. In ordinary discourse, the meaning or intended meaning of words is not always clear. If the sentence begins with the word "everyone", the speaker or writer may have in mind a certain group of people that may be quite different from the group thought of by those listening. We shall learn that in mathematics great care is exercised in the choice of words and that proof has a precise meaning.

Undefined Words

In the past, people sometimes erred in attempting to define every mathematical term they used. This resulted in the use of many definitions that were not precise. It is not possible to define all words or terms in our language, or in any other language for that matter. Definitions of all words in our English dictionary are given by other words. If these words are not meaningful, you may look them up and often, to your dismay, you will discover that the meanings for them are given by using the original word. This is not a fault of your dictionary but only evidence that certain words cannot be defined. Consequently, this circular process cannot be avoided.

Some definitions in the dictionary are simply descriptive; diagrams or pictures are often used to give an intuitive meaning and understanding of the term defined. Such definitions cannot be used as a logical basis for the deductive development of mathematics. This difficulty is avoided in mathematics by recognizing that some words or terms must remain undefined. For example, in geometry, we let such terms as *point, line, plane,* and *space* be undefined. Also, certain relations, such as *congruence of segments* and *betweenness,* are usually left undefined.

Elementary logic and proof

Axioms or Postulates

When we plan to develop an argument or proof, we first select the words or terms that are to remain undefined. We then make statements to indicate the properties which we want the undefined concepts to have. Such statements are called axioms or postulates. The axioms are statements that we assume to be true. It should be clear that it is not necessary for the axioms to be true in any ordinarily accepted sense of the word "truth". We simply assume the axioms to be true for the purpose of developing more mathematics. Having been given some undefined terms and a set of axioms concerning them, we can derive further statements about the undefined terms by using the laws of logic. These further statements are called theorems. We consider all statements to be either true or false, but not both. When a statement is labelled an axiom or postulate, we regard such statement to be true by assumption. Sometimes we cannot be certain whether a further statement is true or false. If its truth can be proved by the use of acceptable deductive methods, we call the statement a *theorem*. A distinguishing characteristic of a deductive system is that, if the axioms are accepted and the methods of reasoning are valid, the theorems that are proved must also be accepted.

Rules of Inference

We shall now discuss a method to prove the consequent of a conditional to be true and thus establish it as the theorem. The basic method of proof is an application of the following *rule of inference*: If the conditional "if p then q" is true, and if p is true, then q is true.

$$[(p \to q) \land p] \to q.$$

We can test the validity of this rule of inference by setting up a truth-table.

p	q	$[(p \to q) \land p]$	$\to$	q
T	T	T	T	T
T	F	F	T	F
F	T	F	T	T
F	F	F	T	F

A proof usually consists of a sequence of steps, each one being justified by an accepted rule of inference. Each step is a sentence. The set of sentences which lead up to the conclusion (theorem to be proved) are known as *premises*. Consequently, in a formal proof we say that we argue from premises to conclusions. An inference which follows from the given premises is said to be a *sound* inference. We can argue *soundly* from

1. True premises to true conclusions,
2. False premises to true conclusions, and
3. False premises to false conclusions,

but false conclusions cannot be obtained from true premises. If we cannot accept the conclusion, we must reject one or more of the premises.

At the beginning of this section, we indicated that $[(p \rightarrow q) \wedge p] \rightarrow q$ was a rule of inference. There are many others, most of which are based on logical implications. In order to develop facility in geometric and algebraic proof, one must have several rules of inference at his command. Following is a short list of rules of inferences:

1. PREMISES: $p \vee q$.

             $\sim p$

  CONCLUSION: q

$$[(p \vee q) \wedge \sim p] \rightarrow q.$$

2. PREMISES: $p \rightarrow q$.

  CONCLUSION: $\sim q \rightarrow \sim p$.

$$(p \rightarrow q) \rightarrow (\sim q \rightarrow \sim p).$$

3. PREMISES: $p \rightarrow q$.

             $\sim p \rightarrow r$.

             $\sim q$

  CONCLUSION: r

$$[(p \rightarrow q) \wedge (\sim p \rightarrow r) \wedge \sim q] \rightarrow r.$$

These rules of inference are *sound*, since all rules of inference, including these three examples, have logical validity. This can be shown by means of truth-tables. Let us test the validity of one of the three examples given, using No. 1 for our sample test.

p	q	$[(p \vee q) \wedge \sim p]$	$\rightarrow$	q
T	T	F	T	T
T	F	F	T	F
F	T	F	T	T
F	F	F	T	F

As there are no false instances, this rule of inference is logically valid.

Truth, Validity, and Soundness

It is important to remember that
1. *Truth* applies to statements,
2. *Validity* applies to statement patterns, and
3. *Soundness* applies to inferences.

Mathematical proof is a *deduction* in which we use a set of statements of which each must be justified. By using a chain of reasons (minor inferences) we establish our conclusion or sound inference.

If we are familiar with rules of inference, we can test the validity of our arguments, whether they be in geometry or algebra. For example, if we argue that:

If triangles a and b are congruent, then triangles a and b are similar.
Triangles a and b are congruent. Therefore triangles a and b are similar.

We can prove this to be true by using a rule of inference as follows:

PREMISES:

1. If triangles a and b are congruent, then triangles a and b are similar.

$$(p \to q).$$

2. Triangles a and b are congruent. (p)

CONCLUSION:

Triangles a and b are similar. (q)

This is our familiar rule $[(p \to q) \land p] \to q$. We have shown this rule to have logical validity. Therefore we can be certain that our conclusion is correct.

In mathematical deductions one is at liberty to assume the validity of rules of inferences, where they apply, as sufficient reason for justifying the truth of any statement. Much of our work in geometry and algebra can be validated more quickly and easily by the appropriate use of rules of inference.

PROBLEMS FOR REVIEW

1. Determine the truth-value of each of the statements expressed below:
   (*a*) $4 + 4 = 8$ and $4 + 5 = 12$.
   (*b*) $2 + 3 = 5$ and $2 \times 4 = 8$.
   (*c*) $3 + 4 = 7$ or $3 \times 3 = 6$.

2. Suppose the conditional, $p \rightarrow q$, is true, what can you say about its converse and its contrapositive?

3. State the converse, inverse, and contrapositive of the following true conditionals. Which of the derived conditionals are true?

(a) If a is an even integer, then $2a$ is divisible by 4.

(b) If the angles of a triangle are all equal, then the triangle is equilateral.

(c) If a rhombus has one right angle, then it is a square.

4. Suppose the biconditional, $p \leftrightarrow q$, is true, what can be said about the following?

$$\sim p \leftrightarrow q.$$
$$p \leftrightarrow \sim q.$$

5. In each of the following examples, determine the truth-value of (ii) under the assumption that each statement expressed in (i) is true:

(a) i. John will go to his office if he is in town.
    He is in town.
    ii. John goes to his office.

(b) i. If it rains, or if Princess Jean is not married, the people will be disappointed.
    The people are not disappointed.
    ii. Princess Jean is married.

6. Show that the biconditional expressed below is logically valid:

$$(p \leftrightarrow q) \leftrightarrow [(p \rightarrow q) \wedge (q \rightarrow p)].$$

BIBLIOGRAPHY

1. ALTWERGER, SAMUEL I. *Modern Mathematics. An Introduction.* New York: The Macmillan Company, 1960.

2. ANDREE, RICHARD V. *Selections from Modern Abstract Algebra.* New York: Henry Holt and Company, 1958.

3. KEMENY, JOHN G., SNELL, J. L. and THOMPSON, GERALD L. *Introduction to Finite Mathematics.* Englewood Cliffs, N. J.: Prentice-Hall, Inc., 1957.

4. MAY, KENNETH O. *Elements of Modern Mathematics.* Addison–Wesley Publishing Company, Reading, Massachusetts, 1959.

5. *Insights into Modern Mathematics.* 23rd Yearbook: National Council of Teachers of Mathematics, 1957. Washington, D.C.

6. *The Growth of Mathematical Ideas.* 24th Yearbook: National Council of Teachers of Mathematics, 1959. Washington, D.C.

7. *Numbers, Statements, and Connectives.* The Mathematics Staff of the College. University of Chicago Press, 1956.

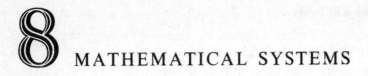

MATHEMATICAL SYSTEMS

DEDUCTIVE SYSTEMS

The words "inductive" and "deductive" are often used to describe methods of reasoning. By inductive methods, we proceed to the solution of problems through experimentation, exploration and observation. In elementary logic, this method is often described as "heuristic", which implies the use of activities that lead to "discovery" By deductive methods, we draw conclusions or make inferences from given premises. Because the given premises are often assumptions or axioms, we say that deductive reasoning is axiomatic in character.

In mathematics, deductive methods give rise to *deductive systems*, of which traditional school geometry is one example. Deductive systems are basic in mathematics, and this chapter will be devoted exclusively to them. However, since we shall lead up to the "discovery" of deductive systems through certain observations, our approach to them may be described as heuristic.

In Chapter 1 we pointed out that, for any deductive mathematical system, we must begin with certain undefined terms and with certain accepted statements or assumptions. Using the undefined terms, we set up definitions for other terms and then develop theorems through the applications of the laws of logic. Later in this chapter we shall derive a more precise and formal definition of a deductive mathematical system.

TWO FAMILIAR SYSTEMS

We shall begin by studying and comparing two familiar operations, the addition of integers and the multiplication of fractions.

1. The Addition of Integers

In various sections of earlier chapters, we discussed the properties of the binary operation of addition on the set of integers (*I*). A summary of the conclusions reached from our observations follows.

(*a*) *Closure law.* If *a* and *b* are replaced by elements of *I*, then for each replacement of *a* and for each replacement of *b*, $a + b$ exists and is a unique element of *I*.

(*b*) *Commutative law.* If *a* and *b* are replaced by elements of *I*, then for each replacement of *a*, and for each replacement of *b*, $a + b = b + a$. The operation of addition is commutative in the set of integers.

(*c*) *Associative law.* If *a*, *b*, and *c* are replaced by elements of *I*, then for each replacement of *a*, and for each replacement of *b*, and for each replacement of *c*, $(a + b) + c = a + (b + c)$. The operation of addition is associative in the set of integers.

(*d*) *Existence of an identity.* An integer zero (0) exists such that for each replacement of *a*, $0 + a = a + 0 = a$; 0 is called the identity element.

(*e*) *Existence of an inverse.* For each replacement of *a*, there exists an integer $-a$, such that $(-a) + a = a + (-a) = 0$; $-a$ is called the additive inverse.

2. The Multiplication of Fractions

Now let us consider the binary operation of multiplication. Our universe is the set of positive fractions (*F*).

(*a*) *Closure law.* If *a* and *b* are replaced by elements of *F*, then for each replacement of *a* and for each replacement of *b*, *ab* exists and is a unique element of *F*.

(*b*) *Commutative law.* If *a* and *b* are replaced by elements of *F*, then for each replacement of *a* and for each replacement of *b*, $ab = ba$. The operation of multiplication is commutative in the set of positive fractions.

(*c*) *Associative law.* If *a*, *b*, and *c* are replaced by elements of *F*, then for each replacement of *a*, and for each replacement of *b*, and for each replacement of *c*, $(ab)c = a(bc)$. The operation of multiplication is associative in the set of positive fractions.

(*d*) *Existence of an identity.* A fraction (1) exists such that for each replacement of *a*, $1a = a1 = a$; 1 is called the identity element for multiplication.

(*e*) *Existence of an inverse.* For each replacement of *a*, there exists a positive fraction $1/a$, such that $1/a \times a = a \times 1/a = 1$; $1/a$ is called the multiplicative inverse of *a*.

Now let us observe certain similarities between the addition of integers and the multiplication of positive fractions. In each case, we had a set of elements and one operation defined on the set. Each of the operations was commutative and associative. Each operation had an identity element in its particular set. Finally, we observed that each of the operations had an inverse element property.

THE COMMUTATIVE GROUP

There are many other systems that possess the five characteristics of the two systems we have discussed. We can generalize from this to establish the existence of an abstract system with these common features. The abstract system in this instance is known as the *commutative group*.

Before we define the commutative group, let us explain what we mean by saying that we can "generalize". First, since we observed that the set of elements in one system may differ from the set of elements in another system, we can say that the set of elements is not specified and denote it simply as set *G*.

Next, we considered an operation on the two systems we discussed, but in each case we considered a different operation. Therefore, we may denote it by a symbol, such as (⋆). Finally, in each system we observed five properties, which we shall call *axioms or postulates*.

This process of generalization leads us to the following definition:

A *commutative group G* is a non-empty set of elements *G* and a binary operation denoted by (⋆), that satisfy the following postulates:

1. *Closure*

If *a* and *b* are replaced by elements of *G*, then for each replacement of *a*, and for each replacement of *b*, $a \star b$ exists and is a unique element of *G*.

2. *Commutative law*

If *a* and *b* are replaced by elements of *G*, then for each replacement of a, and for each replacement of b, $a \star b = b \star a$. The operation ($\star$) is commutative in G.

3. *Associative law*

If a, b, and c are replaced by elements of G, then for each replacement of a, and for each replacement of b, and for each replacement of c,

$$(a \star b) \star c = a \star (b \star c).$$

The operation ($\star$) is associative in G.

4. *Existence of an identity*

An element e exists such that for each replacement of a,

$$e \star a = a \star e = a.$$

e is called the identity element.

5. *Existence of an inverse*

For each replacement of a, there exists an element a^i, such that

$$a^i \star a = a \star a^i = e.$$

The element a^i is called the inverse of a.

Concerning the Structure of the Commutative Group

As we continue our study of the group, we shall learn many things that will deepen our understanding of this mathematical system. It may be helpful at this point to comment further on a few of its features.

1. *The set of elements.* Since the two familiar systems we discussed dealt with numbers (integers and fractions), one may wonder why we do not say the elements of the set are numbers. We do not say so because the elements need not be numbers. We shall learn that they can be something quite different, e.g., motions of some kind. We shall also observe that the set of elements can be finite rather than infinite.

2. *The operation.* In the specific systems we cited, the operations were addition and multiplication. Actually, the operation involved can be something different from addition and multiplication, e.g., successive applications of motions such as rotations. Because of this, it is necessary to say the operation is not specified, and to denote it by some symbol, such as ($\star$).

3. *The identity element.* The identity elements in our two systems were 0 in one case and 1 in the other. Since we shall discover that the identity element is not necessarily 0 or 1, we denote it by e.

4. *The inverse element.* In the two systems that we studied, we denoted the inverse elements by $-a$ and $\frac{1}{a}$. Since we encounter sets in which the inverse cannot be denoted by $-a$ or $\frac{1}{a}$, we therefore use the symbol a^i to represent the inverse of a.

In this book, we shall regard a mathematical system as one which includes a set of elements, one or more operations or relations, postulates, and theorems. That is, a mathematical system includes theorems that can be proved on the basis of the accepted postulates. This is the pattern by which many useful mathematical theorems have been developed.

Theorems for Groups

Now we shall deduce some theorems. This means that we shall obtain from our postulates some additional information about the operation ($\star$). To do this, we shall use logic and the properties of equality. The statements that provide the additional information are called theorems. The examples that follow will show you how to prove a theorem.

EXAMPLE 1: There is exactly one identity element of a group.

We know from postulate (4) that there is at least one identity element. It is e. Now we shall prove that e is unique, i.e., there is only one identity element.

Suppose there is another identity element which we shall denote by e_1. We can then write the following:

(1) $e \star e_1 = e_1 \star e = e_1$.   (Postulate 4)
(2) $e_1 \star e = e \star e_1 = e$.   (Assumption and Postulate 4)
(3) Since $e_1 \star e = e \star e_1$, we conclude that $e_1 = e$.

In other words, the two identity elements are the same and we conclude that e is unique.

EXAMPLE 2: $a \star c = b \star c$, if and only if $a = b$.

Part 1. Assume that $a = b$.

(i) $a \star c = a \star c$ (uniqueness of $\star$).
(ii) $a \star c = b \star c$ (since $a = b$, we may replace the second occurrence of a by b).

Thus if $a = b$, $a \star c = b \star c$.

Part 2. Assume that $a \star c = b \star c$.

(i) $a \star c = b \star c$,   (Assumption)
(ii) c^i exists,   (Postulate 5)
(iii) $(a \star c) \star c^i = (b \star c) \star c^i$,   (Part 1)
(iv) $a \star (c \star c^i) = b \star (c \star c^i)$,   (Postulate 3)
(v) $a \star e = b \star e$,   (Postulate 5)
(vi) $a = b$.   (Postulate 4)

Other Realizations of the Commutative Group

A set of elements and a binary operation defined on the set which satisfies the postulates of a group constitutes a realization of a group. The group itself is called a mathematical model. A realization of this model is an example, or an interpretation, under which the postulates of the model turn out to be true. We have already considered two realizations of the commutative group—the set of integers under addition and the set of positive fractions under multiplication. Now we shall examine the characteristics of two other interpretations of the commutative group.

Modulus 12 System Under Addition

We use another realization of the group model, perhaps quite unconsciously, in our daily routine. Specifically, it involves the hour hand of the clock. Suppose we first consider the operation of addition. If it is now 9 a.m.; five hours later it will be 2 p.m. That is, $9 + 5 = 2$. We might think of this operation as adding 9 and 5, dividing the sum by 12, and using the remainder, 2, as our new sum. In this system, $9 + 5$ is not 14, since 14 is not a clock number. If it is now 8 p.m.; eight hours later it will be 4 a.m. Here, $8 + 8 = 4$. Other addition facts are:

$$7 + 6 = 1.$$
$$8 + 9 = 5.$$
$$7 + 7 + 6 = 8.$$

These number facts are acceptable since in this system there are only twelve numbers. We can set up the addition table as shown on page 171.

Note that we have included the numeral 0 in our table and left out the numeral 12. We may think of 0 as replacing 12 on the clock. We have done this because it is convenient for us to think of the numbers we are using in our set as those numbers that we obtain as remainders when we divide by 12. Of course, we obtain a remainder of 0 whenever we divide a multiple of 12 by 12.

+	0	1	2	3	4	5	6	7	8	9	10	11
0	0	1	2	3	4	5	6	7	8	9	10	11
1	1	2	3	4	5	6	7	8	9	10	11	0
2	2	3	4	5	6	7	8	9	10	11	0	1
3	3	4	5	6	7	8	9	10	11	0	1	2
4	4	5	6	7	8	9	10	11	0	1	2	3
5	5	6	7	8	9	10	11	0	1	2	3	4
6	6	7	8	9	10	11	0	①	2	3	4	5
7	7	8	9	10	11	0	1	2	3	4	5	6
8	8	9	10	11	0	1	2	3	4	5	6	7
9	9	10	11	0	1	2	3	4	5	6	7	8
10	10	11	0	1	2	3	4	5	6	7	8	9
11	11	0	1	2	3	4	5	6	7	8	9	10

To use this table for the operation (+), mod 12, we proceed in this way. Let us consider specific replacements in $a + b$. Let the column to the extreme left include names of replacements for a and the row at the top include names of replacements for b. Suppose a is replaced by 6 and b is replaced by 7. A name for the sum of 6 and 7 is found in the cell to the right of the the numeral 6 and below the numeral 7. We observe that this sum is 1. All tables of this form are read in this manner.

In this type of arithmetic, the number that corresponds to the 12 that we have been using is known as the *modulus* and the mathematical system, *modulus m*, abbreviated *mod m*. We have been discussing non-negative integers modulus 12, or simply mod 12, but we could use any natural number m rather than 12, e.g., 3 or 7. For example, by mod 6, we mean a system in which there are six members: 0, 1, 2, 3, 4, 5.

Now let us return to our consideration of mod 12. First, we note that the number 0 plays the same role as it did in the system of integers under addition. For example, in our system mod 12

$$0 + 2 = 2,$$
$$0 + 4 = 4, \text{ and}$$
$$0 + 6 = 6.$$

Now let us see if $\{0, 1, 2, 3, 4, 5, 6, 7, 8, 9, 10, 11\}$ under the operation of addition satisfies the postulates of the commutative group. We have observed already that we have a set of elements which, in this instance, is finite. We have one operation, which is addition mod 12, and we have zero as the identity element.

The variables a, b, c, which we shall use in our generalizations, may be replaced by elements of $\{0, 1, 2, 3, 4, 5, 6, 7, 8, 9, 10, 11\}$.

1. *Closure law*

If a and b are replaced by elements of our set, then for each replacement of a and for each replacement of b, $a + b$ exists and is a unique element of our set. For example,

$$5 + 6 = 11.$$
$$10 + 4 = 2.$$

2. *Commutative law*

If a and b are replaced by elements of our set, then for each replacement of a and for each replacement of b, $a + b = b + a$. For example,

$$8 + 7 = 7 + 8.$$
$$11 + 5 = 5 + 11.$$

3. *Associative law*

If a, b, and c are replaced by elements of our set, then for each replacement of a, and for each replacement of b, and for each replacement of c, $(a + b) + c = a + (b + c)$. For example,

$$(2 + 6) + 8 = 2 + (6 + 8).$$
$$(8 + 4) + 3 = 8 + (4 + 3).$$

4. *Existence of an identity*

An integer, 0, exists such that for each replacement of a,

$$0 + a = a + 0 = a.$$

Zero is called the identity element. For example,

$$0 + 5 = 5, \qquad 0 + 6 = 6.$$

5. *Existence of an inverse*

For each replacement of a, there exists an integer, $-a$, such that

$$(-a) + a = a + (-a) = 0.$$

The integer $-a$ is called the inverse element. For example, $2 + 10 = 0$, $5 + 7 = 0$. Continuing in this manner, we find that each number in our set has an inverse, mod 12.

Since all the properties of a commutative group are satisfied by the set of integers mod 12, we say the mod 12 system is also a realization of the commutative group under addition.

Now it will be interesting to find out if the mod 12 system is also a realization of the commutative group under multiplication. First, let us consider the operation of multiplication. Some of the multiplication facts are

$$3 \times 8 = 0,$$
$$5 \times 10 = 2, \text{ and}$$
$$4 \times 11 = 8.$$

We may think of these results as the remainders following a division of the product by 12. For example, 4×11 divided by 12 gives a remainder of 8. The multiplication table for mod 12 follows.

×	0	1	2	3	4	5	6	7	8	9	10	11
0	0	0	0	0	0	0	0	0	0	0	0	0
1	0	1	2	3	4	5	6	7	8	9	10	11
2	0	2	4	6	8	10	0	2	4	6	8	10
3	0	3	6	9	0	3	6	9	0	3	6	9
4	0	4	8	0	4	8	0	4	8	0	4	8
5	0	5	10	3	8	1	6	11	4	9	2	7
6	0	6	0	6	0	6	0	6	0	6	0	6
7	0	7	2	9	4	11	6	1	8	3	10	5
8	0	8	4	0	8	4	0	8	4	0	8	4
9	0	9	6	3	0	9	6	3	0	9	6	3
10	0	10	8	6	4	2	0	10	8	6	4	2
11	0	11	10	9	8	7	6	5	4	3	2	1

Considering this system under the operation of multiplication, we can discover through experimentation whether or not each of the five postulates is satisfied. To do this we proceed as we did under the operation of addition. We discover that only four of the five postulates are satisfied. Postulate 5 is not satisfied, since an inverse element does not exist for each a of $\{0, 1, 2, 3, 4, 5, 6, 7, 8, 9, 10, 11\}$.

The number 1 has an inverse, since $1 \times 1 = 1$. However there is no number in our set that 2 can be multiplied by to obtain 1. One is the identity element for multiplication. Therefore, we conclude that we do not have a commutative group in this system under multiplication.

THE ROTATIONS OF AN EQUILATERAL TRIANGLE

This realization of a commutative group will show us that the elements of our set are a finite number of rotations of an equilateral triangle about its centre (centroid). We shall consider only those rotations that bring the triangle into coincidence with itself.

We shall let the the equilateral triangle be *ABC* as illustrated below:

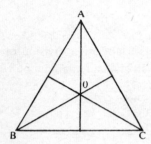

Fig. 126

To facilitate an understanding of this model, cut out an equilateral triangle, letter it as shown, and locate its centre where the medians intersect. The triangle is free to rotate about a pin through the centre 0. First, let us discover each rotation that brings the triangle into coincidence with itself. All rotations are counterclockwise. Through experimentation we shall find that rotations of 120°, 240°, and 360°, and any of these plus a multiple of 360°, will bring the triangle into coincidence with itself. Two rotations are said to be *identical* if they differ from one another by an integral multiple of 360°. The following are examples of identical rotations: 120° and 480°; 240° and 960°. We call the 360° rotation the *zero rotation*, since it leaves the position of the vertices and the sides of the triangle unchanged. All rotations, other than the rotations of 360°, 120°, and 240°, that bring the triangle into coincidence with itself, are identical to one of the three basic rotations. We conclude, therefore, that there are only three rotations to consider in this realization. We shall name them R_0, R_1, and R_2.

These three rotations may be illustrated as follows:

By the addition of two rotations, we mean the combined effect of the first rotation followed by the second. If we add the rotation of 120° to itself, the result is the 240° rotation. If we add the rotation of 120° to the rotation of 240°, the result is the 360° or zero rotation. The binary operation here denoted by (+) is simply the operation "followed by".

We have denoted the three rotations as R_0, R_1, R_2. In other words, the set of elements is $\{R_0, R_1, R_2\}$. Now we can proceed to find out if this system satisfies the postulates of the commutative group under the operation "followed by" (+).

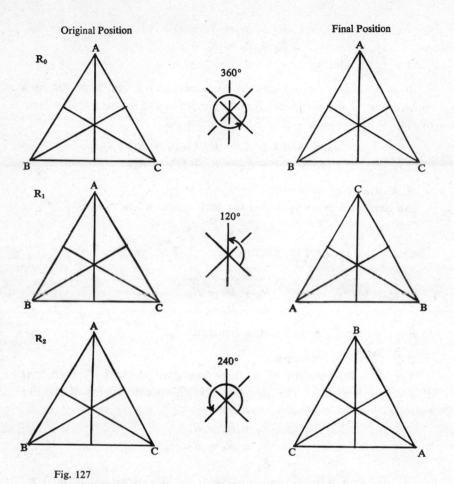

Fig. 127

1. *Closure law*

If a and b are replaced by elements of our set, then for replacement of a and for each replacement of b, $a + b$ exists and is a unique element of our set. For example,

$$R_0 + R_1 = R_1.$$
$$R_1 + R_2 = R_0.$$
$$R_2 + R_0 = R_2.$$

2. *Commutative law*

If a and b are replaced by elements of our set, then for each replacement of a and for each replacement of b, $a + b = b + a$. For example,

$$R_0 + R_1 = R_1 + R_0.$$
$$R_1 + R_2 = R_2 + R_1.$$

3. *Associative law*

If a, b, and c are replaced by elements of our set, then for each replacement of a, and for each replacement of b, and for each replacement of c, $(a + b) + c = a + (b + c)$. For example,

$$(R_0 + R_1) + R_2 = R_0 + (R_1 + R_2).$$
$$(R_1 + R_2) + R_0 = R_1 + (R_2 + R_0).$$

4. *Existence of an identity*

An element e exists such that for each replacement of a,

$$e + a = a + e = a.$$

The element e is called the identity element. For example,

$$R_0 + R_0 = R_0.$$
$$R_0 + R_1 = R_1.$$
$$R_0 + R_2 = R_2.$$

In this instance, R_0 is the identity element.

5. *Existence of an inverse*

For each replacement of a, there exists an element a^i, such that $a^i + a = a + a^i = e$. The element a^i is called the inverse of a. For example,

$$R_0 + R_0 = R_0.$$
$$R_1 + R_2 = R_0.$$
$$R_2 + R_1 = R_0.$$

The inverse of R_0 is R_0, the inverse of R_2 is R_1, and the inverse of R_1 is R_2. From the foregoing equations it is evident that the addition of the inverse to the original rotation results in the identity element.

Since all the postulates are satisfied, we conclude that the rotations of the equilateral triangle under addition, or "followed by", is a realization of the commutative group.

THE GROUP

We have been discussing the mathematical system called the commutative group. There is a common mathematical system known simply as the *group.* This system differs from the commutative group in one respect only. We have observed that the commutative group has five axioms or postulates. The group has only four. The group postulates do not include the commutative postulate. Obviously a commutative group is also a group, but a group is not necessarily a commutative group.

We shall now discuss two realizations of the group. You will observe in each case that the commutative postulate is not satisfied. Thus each example will be a realization of a group that is not a commutative group.

1. The Rotations and Reflections of an Equilateral Triangle

Let *ABC* be an equilateral triangle. As group elements, we shall include the three rotations about the centre of the triangle and three more elements which are the reflections about the medians or axes of the triangle.

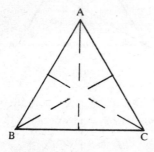 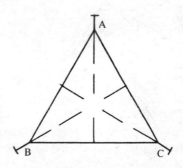

Fig. 128

Our six elements (three rotations about the centre of the triangle and three reflections about the axes of the triangle) may be considered as a finite set of symmetries of an equilateral triangle. We define symmetries of a triangle as motions that bring the triangle into coincidence with itself. Before proceeding, it should be established that each of the six elements is a symmetry. Rotations of the triangle about its centre have been discussed earlier. Reflections of the triangle are obtained by turning the triangle over about the pins inserted in each vertex along the axis as shown in Figures 128 and 129. This turning motion is one of 180° in order to bring the triangle in coincidence with itself.

Since there are three medians, which we refer to as the axes of the triangle, there are three reflections. We shall denote them by R_3, R_4, and R_5. These reflections are illustrated below.

178 ✻

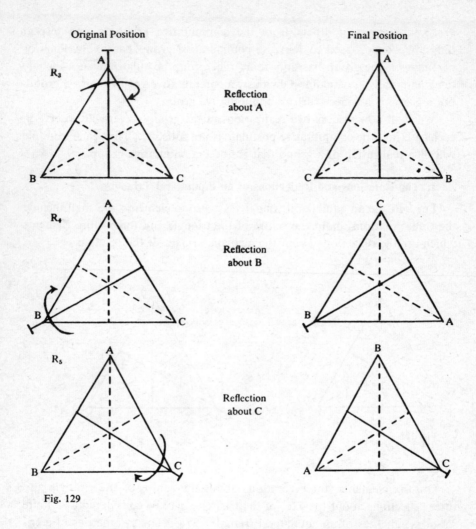

Original Position   Final Position

R_3 A   A

          Reflection
          about A

B _____ C   C _____ B

R_4 A   C

          Reflection
          about B

B _____ C   B _____ A

R_5 A   B

          Reflection
          about C

B _____ C   A _____ C

Fig. 129

Now let us observe some properties of this interpretation under the operation of addition, which we shall denote by (+). The binary operation (+) for this system may be defined as follows: If x and y are replaced by any two of the six motions, the result $x + y$ is the motion that results when the replacement for x is performed first and then followed by the replacement for y.

Our set of elements in this system may be denoted by $K = \{R_0, R_1, R_2, R_3, R_4, R_5\}$. We can now write the following sentences and verify each by performing the operation (+) as indicated with a cut-out triangle.

$$R_0 + R_2 = R_2.$$
$$R_4 + R_3 = R_2.$$
$$R_3 + R_4 = R_1.$$
$$(R_2 + R_4) + R_5 = R_0.$$
$$R_2 + (R_4 + R_5) = R_0.$$
$$R_4 + R_4 = R_0.$$

Many more sentences may be written.

In the following discussion, we shall use variables a, b, and c. These variables may be replaced by elements of K.

1. *The closure law is satisfied*

If a and b are replaced by elements of K, then for each replacement of a and for each replacement of b, $a + b$ exists and is a unique element of K. For example,

$$R_4 + R_3 = R_2.$$

2. *The associative law is satisfied*

If a, b, and c are replaced by elements of K, then for each replacement of a, and for each replacement of b, and for each replacement of c, $(a + b) + c = a + (b + c)$. For example,

$$(R_1 + R_3) + R_5 = R_1 + (R_3 + R_5).$$

3. *The existence of an identity*

An element e exists such that for each replacement of a,

$$e + a = a + e = a.$$

The element e is called the identity element. For example,

$$R_0 + R_2 = R_2.$$
$$R_0 + R_4 = R_4.$$

R_0 is the identity element.

4. *The existence of an inverse*

For each replacement of a, there exists an element, $-a$, such that $(-a) + a = a + (-a) = 0$. The element $-a$ is called the inverse element.

$$R_0 + R_0 = R_0.$$
$$R_1 + R_2 = R_0.$$
$$R_2 + R_1 = R_0.$$

The inverse of R_1 is R_2, and the inverse of R_2 is R_1. Each of R_0, R_3, R_4, R_5 is its own inverse.

Further study will show that the four postulates for a group are satisfied. We may conclude that the six symmetries of an equilateral triangle form a realization of a group under addition.

We should note that this system is not a realization of the commutative group since the commutative property is not satisfied. For example, sentences (2) and (3) tell us that $R_4 + R_3 \neq R_3 + R_4$.

2. Permutations of Three Numbers

For our second realization of a group that is not a commutative group, we shall use permutations of three numbers. We think of a permutation as a change of position, order, or arrangement. For example, if a number of boys are seated on a bench, a permutation takes place every time there is a change in the seating arrangement. We can speak of permutations of any set of objects. Since the choice of objects is arbitrary, we may denote them by symbols such as letters of the alphabet or numerals. Let us consider, therefore, the permutations of the three numbers 1, 2, and 3.

We shall choose to denote each permutation as follows:

$$a = \begin{pmatrix} 1 & 2 & 3 \\ 2 & 3 & 1 \end{pmatrix}$$

is understood to mean that each number expressed in the top row is replaced by the number named directly below it. That is, in the preceding illustration, 1 is replaced by 2, 2 is replaced by 3, and 3 is replaced by 1.

The six possible permutations (or substitutions) are:

$$a = \begin{pmatrix} 1 & 2 & 3 \\ 1 & 2 & 3 \end{pmatrix}. \qquad d = \begin{pmatrix} 1 & 2 & 3 \\ 2 & 3 & 1 \end{pmatrix}.$$

$$b = \begin{pmatrix} 1 & 2 & 3 \\ 1 & 3 & 2 \end{pmatrix}. \qquad e = \begin{pmatrix} 1 & 2 & 3 \\ 3 & 1 & 2 \end{pmatrix}.$$

$$c = \begin{pmatrix} 1 & 2 & 3 \\ 2 & 1 & 3 \end{pmatrix}. \qquad f = \begin{pmatrix} 1 & 2 & 3 \\ 3 & 2 & 1 \end{pmatrix}.$$

We shall now consider these six permutations as elements of a set S, in which the operation $(+)$ is the successive application of two permutations. $a + b$ means "a followed by b", or "do a and then do b".

Now let us write down a few results of successive applications of two permutations under the operation.

$$a + b = \begin{pmatrix} 1 & 2 & 3 \\ 1 & 2 & 3 \end{pmatrix} + \begin{pmatrix} 1 & 2 & 3 \\ 1 & 3 & 2 \end{pmatrix} = \begin{pmatrix} 1 & 2 & 3 \\ 1 & 3 & 2 \end{pmatrix} = b.$$

$$c + d = \begin{pmatrix} 1 & 2 & 3 \\ 2 & 1 & 3 \end{pmatrix} + \begin{pmatrix} 1 & 2 & 3 \\ 2 & 3 & 1 \end{pmatrix} = \begin{pmatrix} 1 & 2 & 3 \\ 3 & 2 & 1 \end{pmatrix} = f.$$

$$d + e = \begin{pmatrix} 1 & 2 & 3 \\ 2 & 3 & 1 \end{pmatrix} + \begin{pmatrix} 1 & 2 & 3 \\ 3 & 1 & 2 \end{pmatrix} = \begin{pmatrix} 1 & 2 & 3 \\ 1 & 2 & 3 \end{pmatrix} = a.$$

Let us explain one of the above, for example, $c + d$. We shall do c and then do d. First, c says replace 1 by 2, and d says replace 2 by 3. As a result 3 will be where 1 was originally. Secondly, c says replace 2 by 1, and d says replace 1 by 2, which results in 2 regaining its original place. Finally, c says replace 3 by 3 (no change), and d says replace 3 by 1. As a result 1 will be where 3 was originally. In other words, the numbers 1, 2, 3 now have the arrangement 3, 2, 1. To indicate this we write

$$\begin{pmatrix} 1 & 2 & 3 \\ 3 & 2 & 1 \end{pmatrix}$$

which is permutation f.

The following table indicates all possible results of successive applications of two permutations:

Second Term

+	a	b	c	d	e	f
a	a	b	c	d	e	f
b	b	a	d	c	f	e
c	c	e	a	f	b	d
d	d	f	b	e	a	c
e	e	c	f	a	d	b
f	f	d	e	b	c	a

First Term

We have noted that in this realization of a group, the set of elements S, is the six permutations, a, b, c, d, e, f, and that the operation is $(+)$, which means "followed by". We shall use variables x, y, and z. These variables may be replaced by elements of S.

1. *Closure law*

If x and y are replaced by elements of S, then for each replacement of x, and for each replacement of y, $x + y$ exists and is a unique element of S. For example,

$$a + b = b,$$
$$b + c = d, \text{ and}$$
$$e + c = f.$$

2. *Associative law*

If x, y, and z are replaced by elements of S, then for each replacement of x, and for each replacement of y, and for each replacement of z, $(x + y) + z = x + (y + z)$. For example,

$$(b + c) + d = e, \text{ and}$$
$$b + (c + d) = e.$$

Also,
$$(c + e) + d = c, \text{ and}$$
$$c + (e + d) = c.$$

3. *Existence of an identity*

An element a in our set exists such that for each replacement of x, $a + x = x + a = x$. The element a is called the identity element. For example,

$$a + a = a,$$
$$a + b = b,$$
$$a + c = c,$$
$$a + d = d,$$
$$a + e = e, \text{ and}$$
$$a + f = f.$$

Therefore, a is the identity element.

4. *Existence of an inverse*

For each replacement of x, there exists an element x^i, such that $x^i + x = x + x^i = a$. (Recall that the element a has been shown to be our identity element in this system.) The element x^i is called the inverse of x. For example,

$$a + a = a,$$
$$b + b = a,$$
$$c + c = a,$$
$$f + f = a,$$
$$d + e = a, \text{ and}$$
$$e + d = a.$$

We conclude that each of the six elements has an inverse.

This realization of a group is not a commutative group since

$$b + c = d, \text{ and}$$
$$c + b = e.$$

Thus $b + c \neq c + b$.

OTHER MATHEMATICAL SYSTEMS

We are now fairly familiar with the group. There are other mathematical systems that are important and useful, such as the *field*, *integral domain*, and *ring*. We shall not examine all of them, since our purpose in this chapter is simply to introduce the concept of a mathematical system and to become acquainted with two or three specific realizations. At this point, let us consider the mathematical system known as the field.

Field

We have observed that the group involves one operation, which may be addition or multiplication, or some other operation for a specific realization. There are mathematical systems that involve two operations which we may denote by $\star$ and $\odot$. Perhaps the most important system of this type is the field.

A field is defined as a set of elements, which we shall denote by F, having two operations, addition ($\star$) and multiplication ($\odot$), which satisfy the following postulates. (Addition and multiplication do not necessarily mean ordinary addition and multiplication.)

1. *Closure laws for addition and multiplication*

If a and b are replaced by elements of F, then for each replacement of a, and for each replacement of b, $a \star b$ and $a \odot b$ exist and are both unique elements of F.

2. *Commutative laws for addition and multiplication*

If a and b are replaced by elements of F, then for each replacement of a, and for each replacement of b, $a \star b = b \star a$, and $a \odot b = b \odot a$. The operations ($\star$) and ($\odot$) are commutative in F.

3. *Associative laws for addition and multiplication*

If a, b, and c are replaced by elements of F, then for each replacement of a, and for each replacement of b, and for each replacement of c,

$$(a \star b) \star c = a \star (b \star c), \text{ and}$$

$$(a \odot b) \odot c = a \odot (b \odot c).$$

The operations ($\star$) and ($\odot$) are associative in F.

4. *Identity for addition*

An element e exists such that for each replacement of a,

$$e \star a = a \star e = a.$$

The element e is called the identity element for addition. In many realizations of a field e is zero (0).

5. *Identity for multiplication*

An element i exists such that for each replacement of a,

$$i \odot a = a \odot i = a.$$

The element i is called the identity element for multiplication. In many realizations of a field i is unity (1).

6. *Inverse law of addition*

For each replacement of a, there exists an element a^i such that $a^i \star a = a \star a^i = e$. The element a^i is called the additive inverse of a. In many realizations of a field a^i is $-a$.

7. *Inverse law for multiplication*

For each replacement of a, except e, there exists an element ^-a such that $^-a \odot a = a \odot {^-a} = i$. In many realizations of a field ^-a is $1/a$.

8. *Distributive law*

If a, b, and c are replaced by elements of F, then for each replacement of a, and for each replacement of b, and for each replacement of c,

$$a \odot (b \star c) = a \odot b \star a \odot c.$$

That is, multiplication distributes over addition.

Any mathematical system having these properties is a field. The reader should convince himself that the set of real numbers relative to addition and multiplication possesses all the properties expressed above. Thus the set of real numbers relative to addition and multiplication is an interpretation of a field.

The properties of the real number system form an axiomatic foundation for most of elementary algebra. Most of the processes and theorems of elementary algebra can be proved by deductive reasoning on the basis of the properties of the real number system. The theorems expressed below are just a few of these. We include the proofs of two of them. The universe is the set of real numbers.

THEOREM 1: For each replacement of a and for each replacement of b, if $a + b = a + c$, then $b = c$.

THEOREM 2: The additive identity for the system of real numbers is unique.

THEOREM 3: The additive inverse of a real number is unique.

THEOREM 4: For each replacement of a, $a \cdot 0 = 0$ and $0 \cdot a = 0$.

THEOREM 5: For each replacement of a and for each replacement of b, $a(-b) = -(ab)$ and $(-a)b = -(ab)$.

THEOREM 6: For each replacement of a and for each replacement of b, $(-a)(-b) = ab$.

THEOREM 7: For each replacement of a and for each replacement of b, $a \cdot b = 0$ if and only if $a = 0$ or $b = 0$.

PROOF OF THEOREM 4: For each replacement of a, $a \cdot 0 = 0$ and $0 \cdot a = 0$.
(1) $a(0 + 0) = a \cdot 0 + a \cdot 0$. (distributive property)
(2) $a(0 + 0) = a \cdot 0$. (additive identity)
(3) $a \cdot 0 + a \cdot 0 = a \cdot 0$. (transitive property of equality)
(4) $a \cdot 0 = 0$. (additive identity and theorem 2)
(5) $0 \cdot a = 0$. (commutative property and transitive property of equality)

PROOF OF THEOREM 7: For each replacement of a and for each replacement of b, $a \cdot b = 0$ if and only if $a = 0$ or $b = 0$.

Part One

(1) $a = 0$. (hypothesis)
(2) $a \cdot b = 0$. (theorem 4)

Part Two

If $a = 0$, the proof is done. If $a \neq 0$, then $\dfrac{1}{a}$ exists by the inverse property for multiplication.

(1) $ab = 0$.   (hypothesis)

(2) $\dfrac{1}{a} = \dfrac{1}{a}.$ (reflexive property of equality)

(3) $\dfrac{1}{a}(ab) = \dfrac{1}{a}(0).$ (well-defined property of multiplication)

(4) $\left(\dfrac{1}{a} \cdot a\right) b = 0.$ (associative property and theorem 4)

(5) $1 \cdot b = 0$.   (inverse property)

(6) $b = 0$.   (multiplicative identity)

Now let us consider an interpretation of the field.

Modulus 7

Since we have discussed the finite system, modulus 12, as a realization of a group, it will not be difficult to consider a system, modulus 7, as a realization of a field. Our set is the set of numbers $\{0, 1, 2, 3, 4, 5, 6\}$. These are the possible remainders that we can obtain upon dividing any non-negative integer by the number 7. We can define addition and multiplication as we did previously. The sum of any two members of our set is found by obtaining the usual sum and then dividing this usual sum by 7. The new sum is the remainder that we obtain by dividing the original sum by 7. Our new product is the product we obtain by first dividing our original product by 7 and then taking the remainder.

Now let us see if the postulates of the field are satisfied by our mod 7 system.

1. *Closure.* We can set up the addition and multiplication tables for the modulus 7 system as follows:

+	0	1	2	3	4	5	6
0	0	1	2	3	4	5	6
1	1	2	3	4	5	6	0
2	2	3	4	5	6	0	1
3	3	4	5	6	0	1	2
4	4	5	6	0	1	2	3
5	5	6	0	1	2	3	4
6	6	0	1	2	3	4	5

×	0	1	2	3	4	5	6
0	0	0	0	0	0	0	0
1	0	1	2	3	4	5	6
2	0	2	4	6	1	3	5
3	0	3	6	2	5	1	4
4	0	4	1	5	2	6	3
5	0	5	3	1	6	4	2
6	0	6	5	4	3	2	1

Let us denote our set of elements by S. From the tables above, it is observed that if a and b are elements of S, then for each replacement of a, and for each replacement of b, $a + b$ and $a \times b$ exist, and are both unique elements of S. Therefore, we conclude that the *closure laws* are satisfied.

2. For each replacement of a and for each replacement of b, it can be shown (use addition table) that

$$a + b = b + a.$$

Similarly for each replacement of a and for each replacement of b it can be shown (use multiplication table) that

$$a \times b = b \times a.$$

The reader should verify that the *commutative laws* for addition and multiplication (mod 7) are satisfied.

3. For each replacement of a, and for each replacement of b, and for each replacement of c, it can be shown that

$$(a + b) + c = a + (b + c), \text{ and}$$
$$(a \times b) \times c = a \times (b \times c).$$

Therefore, the *associative laws* for addition and multiplication are satisfied.

4. The addition table indicates that there exists an element 0 in S, such that for each replacement of a, $0 + a = a + 0 = a$. For example, $0 + 2 = 2$, $0 + 4 = 4$. We conclude that there is an *additive identity* (zero).

5. The multiplication table indicates that there is an element 1 in S, such that for each replacement of a, $1 \times a = a \times 1 = a$. For example, $1 \times 3 = 3$, $1 \times 5 = 5$. Hence, 1 *is the multiplicative identity*.

6. Using the addition table, we can write the following:

$$0 + 0 = 0$$
$$6 + 1 = 1 + 6 = 0$$
$$5 + 2 = 2 + 5 = 0$$
$$4 + 3 = 3 + 4 = 0$$
$$3 + 4 = 4 + 3 = 0$$
$$2 + 5 = 5 + 2 = 0$$
$$1 + 6 = 6 + 1 = 0$$

We observe that for each element a, there exists an element $-a$, such that for each replacement of a, $(-a) + a = a + (-a) = 0$. The element $-a$ is the additive inverse of a. We conclude that the *inverse law for addition* is satisfied.

7. Using the multiplication table, we can write the following:

$$1 \times 1 = 1$$
$$4 \times 2 = 2 \times 4 = 1$$
$$5 \times 3 = 3 \times 5 = 1$$
$$2 \times 4 = 4 \times 2 = 1$$
$$3 \times 5 = 5 \times 3 = 1$$
$$6 \times 6 = 1$$

For each non-zero replacement of a in S, there exists an element $1/a$ such that $1/a \times a = a \times 1/a = 1$. This indicates that the *inverse law for multiplication* is satisfied.

8. Using both the addition and multiplication tables, we can write

$$2 \times (3 + 5) = 2 \times 3 + 2 \times 5, \text{ and}$$
$$4 \times (2 + 3) = 4 \times 2 + 4 \times 3.$$

We can verify that multiplication distributes over addition. Therefore we conclude that the *distributive law* is satisfied.

Since all the field postulates have been satisfied, we conclude that the mod 7 system is a realization of the field.

CONCLUSION

In Chapter 3, we discussed some of the number systems. A number system (abstract) is another kind of mathematical system. We observed that a subset of the fractions, the positive fractions, forms a realization of a group. By further study, we could discover that all the fractions form a field. The integers form a realization of a mathematical system known as an *integral domain*. They do not form a realization of a field.

All mathematical models are abstract, but each has several interpretations or realizations, and each includes a number of theorems. All theorems of a model apply to any realization of the model. For example, the theorems we develop from the field postulates apply to any realization of the field. The concept of mathematical models gives facility and power to mathematical applications and developments.

PROBLEMS FOR REVIEW

1. Following is the addition table for a particular mathematical model:

+	a b c d
a	b c d a
b	c d a b
c	d a b c
d	a b c d

   Show whether or not the commutative and associative postulates for addition are satisfied by this model.

2. Construct the addition and multiplication tables for the non-negative integers modulus 6.

3. Do the non-negative integers modulus 6 form a realization of a field?

4. Do the non-negative integers modulus 4 form a realization of a group under multiplication?

5. Does the set $\{0, 2, 4, 6, \ldots\}$ form a realization of a commutative group under addition?

6. Show that the elements of a field form a group under addition.

7. Show that the set of odd positive integers does not form a realization of a field.

8. Solve the following in the modulus 6 system:

   (a) $3 + 2 + 3 + 4 + 5$.
   (b) $4 + 5 + 3$.
   (c) $3x = 5$.
   (d) $x^2 = 2$.
   (e) $x^3 = 6$.
   (f) $4x^2 + 3 = 2$.

9. Using the field postulates, solve the equation

$$2 + 4a = 2 - 3.$$

   The universe is the set of real numbers.

BIBLIOGRAPHY

1. ADLER, IRVING. *The New Mathematics*. New York: The John Day Company, 1958.

2. ALLENDOERFER, C. B. and OAKLEY, C. O. *Principles of Mathematics*. Toronto: McGraw-Hill Book Company, Inc., 1955.

3. ALEXANDROFF, P. S. *Introduction to the Theory of Groups*. Toronto: The Ryerson Press, 1959.

4. ANDREE, RICHARD V. *Selections from Modern Abstract Algebra*. New York: Henry Holt and Company, 1958.

5. MAY, KENNETH O. *Elements of Modern Mathematics*. London, England: Addison-Wesley Publishing Company, Inc., 1959.

6. *Insights into Modern Mathematics*. 23rd Yearbook: National Council of Teachers of Mathematics, 1957. Washington D.C.

9 SOME BASIC MATHEMATICAL IDEAS AND THEIR IMPLICATIONS FOR THE SCHOOL PROGRAM

The ideas developed in this book have implications at all levels of the school mathematics program. Although the topics that have been discussed appear to relate only to the secondary school program, there are many implications in them for elementary arithmetic.

It would be most difficult to designate the grade or grades particularly affected by each topic. For example, number systems and problem solving are not restricted to one section of the program but are developed and extended at all levels. Thus it appears necessary to consider the reorganization of the total school mathematics program. In other words, merely adding to and subtracting from the traditional program will not meet the real need for a new and better treatment of school mathematics.

The discussion of topics in the preceding chapters has been intentionally brief, although several important areas of modern mathematics were considered in a sequential manner in order to show relationships and to maintain continuity. The purpose of this book has been to present an overview of these topics. Those readers who choose to delve more deeply into any or all of them may do so by reading one or more of the recent publications on modern mathematics. However, since much of the present literature on this subject is written for the serious student of mathematics, one should first have an understanding of the new point of view, the many fundamental principles, and the new terminology and notation before attempting to read more advanced books. In this book, an attempt has been made to meet the needs of most of those readers who must start from the very beginning to learn these essential principles and techniques.

In this final chapter, we could discuss the implications of each topic in sequence as it appears in the text, or we might discuss the implications of the major concepts that thread through the entire text. These are the concepts that would, in fact, permeate and integrate an entire school progam. We have chosen the latter approach, believing it to be more effective in clarifying and consolidating a meaningful program in mathematics.

In each instance, first attention has been given to implications for the elementary program. This has been done because it is reasonable to start with the primary grades. The chief purpose is to indicate that there are definite implications, although no attempt is made to point out more than a few of them.

SETS AND CONDITIONS

The notion of a set is basic to mathematics. It has been used in the development of material in each of the chapters of this book. It need not be treated as a separate area in mathematics, but may be taken as fundamental to all of them. It is a powerful unifying concept which helps to clarify many mathematical principles.

Mathematics is essentially an abstract science, but it is built up initially from observations in the physical world. In Grade 1, children first experience a feeling for number by considering sets of objects. Formal terminology and notation of sets need not be introduced until early in the secondary school grades, but we may find through experimentation that elementary set language can be used to advantage and with understanding in the elementary grades. The notion of an operation as a mapping can be used to explain the basic operations in elementary arithmetic. In order to do this, we must talk about operations defined on sets of numbers, and of certain sets of numbers closed under certain operations. Again, when we study fractions, we consider sets of equivalent fractions.

Set algebra might well be introduced early in the senior high school grades. The algebra with which most of us are familiar may be called number algebra since the elements used are numbers. In set algebra, the elements are sets. In number algebra, we have the two common binary operations of addition and multiplication, while in set algebra we have binary operations that form the union and intersection of sets. In number algebra we must have coefficients and exponents. For example, in $a + a = 2a$, 2 is a coefficient and in $a \times a = a^2$ the 2 is an exponent. In set algebra, we do not require coefficients or exponents since $A \cup A = A$, and $A \cap A = A$.

There are many reasons for studying set algebra. The chief purpose is to give the student a chance to make comparisons. When he studies the properties of the different operations, he observes similarities and differences between the two algebras. In this way, he comes to see that the properties of operations on numbers are not identical with the properties of operations on sets. A greater understanding of both systems, and a deeper insight into the general nature of mathematics, should result from this comparison. In our discussion of modern mathematics we have introduced the study of mathematical systems, such as the group and the field. Such mathematical systems are more readily understood by students after they become familiar with systems whose elements are sets, as well as with systems whose elements are numbers.

We have observed the importance of such concepts as *universe, variable, condition,* and *solution set.* By the consideration of specific sets, we have developed the concept of *universe.* Through the concepts of universe and condition, we have established the notion of a *variable.* Using set notation and terminology, we have built up the concept of *solution set* of a condition. The consideration of solution sets of conditions in two variables led us to the study of *relations* and *functions.* Thus we see that the notion of a set has many implications throughout the school program.

The concept of a set should originate in Grade 1 and be developed throughout the succeeding grades. Its treatment in the early grades may be somewhat incidental, but in the junior high school grades specific attention should be given to the descriptive theory of sets, and its application to the study of relations and functions. Some set algebra may be introduced early in the senior high school, and a variety of mathematical systems may be surveyed in the later years of senior high school. It is impossible to suggest definite grade placement of many such topics until further research and classroom experimentation have been carried out.

ONE-TO-ONE CORRESPONDENCE

The concept of one-to-one correspondence is basic in elementary arithmetic as well as in secondary school mathematics. For example, we develop the concept of number by considering sets of objects that can be placed in one-to-one correspondence. When the elements of two sets can be placed in a one-to-one correspondence, the two sets are *equivalent.* Equivalent sets have the same cardinal number. By setting up a one-to-one correspondence between one set and a proper subset of another set, we develop the notion of "is less than". We can then use "is less than" to order the cardinal numbers.

After considerable experience with equivalent sets and standard sets, we learn to count by finding the standard set that is equivalent to the set of objects to be counted. Thus we develop skill in rational counting using the concept of one-to-one correspondence. Rote counting, which is merely saying the numerals in order after memorization, is quite a different process.

The concept of one-to-one correspondence was further clarified when we observed the relationship between mappings and one-to-one correspondence. It was noted, also, that the binary operations of addition and multiplication are examples of many-to-one mappings. We shall make further reference to mappings and one-to-one correspondence under the headings of "Relations" and "Problem Solving".

NUMBERS AND NUMBER SYSTEMS

Let S be a given set and let addition and multiplication be operations defined on S. If addition and multiplication are each commutative and associative, and if multiplication distributes over addition, we say that S is a number system with respect to addition and multiplication. Elements of such sets are called numbers.

The *natural numbers* under addition and multiplication make up our first number system. The set is *closed* under the operations of addition and multiplication. This means that the sum or product of any two natural numbers is also a natural number. However, we cannot always subtract in the system of natural numbers and obtain a difference that is a natural number. Thus it is necessary to extend this number system to the system of *integers*. Similarly, since this system is not closed under the operation of division, it is necessary to extend again to build the system of *rational numbers*. Finally, we are able to develop the *real number* system. It was indicated that "extension" could take us beyond the reals, for example, to *complex numbers*. Thus we learn that we do not have one number system but several.

During the first two or three years of school, children become well acquainted with numbers as properties of sets. These are the finite cardinals or natural numbers defined in terms of standard sets. It has always been customary (and still is) to introduce fractions following work with natural numbers. Considering the manner in which we developed the real number system early in the text, we may conclude that there is a definite implication that the system of integers might be developed and studied before the introduction of fractions. No doubt the chief reason for considering fractions before integers is the fact that children require an early knowledge of fractions because of the social environment in which they grow and work. However, the possibility of introducing integers before fractions should not be ruled out without further study and experimentation. Either method is mathematically sound. The one that is more satisfying psychologically should be chosen.

Because the natural numbers are closed under the operations of addition and multiplication, and because of the commutative property, no precautions need to be taken concerning the order in which numbers are added or multiplied. However, in the matter of subtraction we are careful always to protect ourselves by having the pupils subtract a given number from a greater number. When children see that they cannot reverse the order of subtraction, there should be no reason why the integers cannot be introduced. Certainly children do have some experience with applications of integers. A common example is the reading of temperatures on a thermometer. We do not propose a plan of action, but we do imply the need for experimentation in this area.

Now, let us consider the importance of the basic properties of the addition and multiplication operations. Many teachers find it difficult to see how a knowledge of the properties of these operations can be of much assistance in arithmetic instruction. This is understandable. Indeed, the teaching of arithmetic without this knowledge is not too disturbing to many teachers. Undoubtedly, they fail to see that it is a difficult and time-consuming task to learn the infinite number of arithmetical facts and processes without the generalizations which these properties provide. Many believe that traditional programs in mathematics have lacked basic structure and power, and that students have been handicapped in their progress, because we have made little use of the properties, even in high school mathematics.

In the elementary grades, a study of the properties of the operations helps students understand the various algorithms that are used in the computational processes. A study of the properties of the operations also gives students increased insight into the meaning of the operations, and a better understanding of the relationship between an operation and its inverse operation.

The basic properties of the operations are extremely important in secondary mathematics. As we have already mentioned, an understanding of the properties of the operations is necessary in order to achieve an understanding of the meaning of a mathematical system, which leads to an understanding of what we mean by structure in mathematics. Also, secondary school students can achieve an understanding of the manipulations that are performed in ordinary algebra, if they understand the basic properties of the operations.

RELATIONS

Certainly a major and specific characteristic of mathematics is the frequent use made of the concept of *ordered pairs*. A set of ordered pairs of numbers is a mathematical concept that is of considerable significance at all levels of a mathematical program. Even in the lives of very young children, the ordered pair idea is very commonplace. For example, they often pair amounts of money with pieces of candy or with cones of ice cream. In the elementary grades, the study of fractions involves the study of ordered pairs. In the secondary school, when we encounter conditions in two variables, we are led to the study of relations and functions. In fact, we define a relation as a set of ordered pairs and a function as a special relation in which no two pairs have the same first component.

Since a thorough study of relations simplifies the study of functions, it would seem logical for students to spend several months (in junior high school) on the study of relations before they begin to study functions. This suggests a subject area quite different from anything found in traditional programs.

In Chapters 4, 5, and 6, we observed that in many instances ordered pairs played a prominent rôle in finding and graphing solution sets of equations and inequalities, determining coordinates in the Cartesian plane, and developing the algebra of relations, elementary functions and inverse functions. In all cases, there are many implications for a school program in mathematics. In Chapter 6, we observed that the binary operations, such as addition and multiplication, can be regarded as mappings from $I \times I$ to I or from $D \times D$ to D. Here again the concept of a set of ordered pairs is central. In these binary operations, the first component of each ordered pair is itself an ordered pair of $I \times I$ or $D \times D$, and the second component of each ordered pair is an element of I or D. For example, when we multiply 2 and 3, the ordered pair that is a member of the function is $((2, 3), 6)$. Remember that whenever we have a set of ordered pairs we have a relation.

Finally, in this section we mention a relation that is encountered very frequently by students. Examples are problems involving cost per article, miles per hour, and per cent. Any relation is a set of ordered pairs. If the ordered pairs of a relation are of the form (ak, bk) or $\dfrac{ak}{bk}$, the relation is said to be a set of rate pairs and is known as a rate-pair or a proportional relation. Each member of a proportional relation is equivalent to each of the other members. The relation $\{(2, 3), (4, 6), (6, 9), (8, 12)\}$ is an example of a proportional relation.

You will observe that each pair in this set is of the form (ak, bk), which in this case is $(2k, 3k)$. For the first pair k is replaced by 1; for the second pair k replaced by 2; for the third pair k is replaced by 3; etc. An ordered pair such as $(5, 6)$ does not belong to this relation since we cannot replace k in $(2k, 3k)$ by any number that would yield $(5, 6)$. Names of rate pairs are called ratios.

NAMES AND THEIR REFERENTS

To think and write about mathematics, we must have and use a language with precise and clear meaning. Toward this end, we must distinguish between the names of objects and the objects themselves. We speak of the object to which a name refers as the *referent* of the name.

In this book we observed that names of numbers are quite different from the numbers themselves. Names of numbers are known as numerals. The system we use to name numbers is called a numeration system. We write the numerals 5 and 7 to name the numbers five and seven. In the Roman system of numeration, we would write the numerals V and VII. We use the Hindu–Arabic system of numeration. The number-numeral distinction is of importance in the school program commencing in Grade 1. Here the children learn that each number can have more than one name. For example, the child learns he can have the numerals 7, 3 + 4, 2 + 5, and 1 + 6 as names for the number seven. Similarly, each rational number has several names. For example, the numerals 6/8, 9/12, and 12/16 are all names for the same rational number.

Throughout a mathematics program there are several instances in which distinctions can and should be made between names and their referents. In the study of sentences, we learned that the referent of a closed sentence is a statement and the referent of an open sentence is a condition. In open sentences, we encounter placeholders whose referents are variables. For example, in the open sentence $x + y = 6$, the letters x and y are place-holders. The replacement set for these placeholders are numerals. The referents of the placeholders are variables whose replacement set is a set of numbers. The referent of the open sentence is a condition. The condition contains the variables. The replacements made for x and y must have a sum of 6 in order to satisfy the condition $x + y = 6$.

The name-referent concept has implications for the entire mathematics program. The number-numeral distinction should be made in the elementary school grades. Since the notions of statements, conditions, placeholders, and variables are basic to all areas of mathematics, it would be well if such concepts could be introduced in upper elementary school grades and in the junior high school.

PROOF

We have said that proof is important to everyone. In the early grades we do not attempt to develop formal proof. It is not needed at that stage and, furthermore, methods of deductive proof are too involved and sophisticated for young students. As in many other areas of mathematics, we advance one step at a time in accordance with our needs and the level of our under-standing. For example, in the elementary grades, we begin to make generali-zations. We discover, for instance, that $2 + 3$ is the same as $3 + 2$. In the junior high school grades, we make a more formal generalization and write the sentence $a + b = b + a$. Our understanding of this generalization improves when we learn to use replacement language and to say "for each replacement of a and for each replacement of b, a true statement is obtained from $a + b = b + a$". In the senior high school grades, we come to regard this property as a basic postulate of a number system and to use it in formal proofs. Finally, by adding other postulates we learn how to build and use a mathematical system such as the field. At this point, we discover that we have the machinery necessary for justifying the work in ordinary algebra.

In the senior high school, the student should develop a facility and under-standing of deductive reasoning. We have observed that deductive methods are basic in mathematics and, in the modern approach, receive increased emphasis. In developing and working with mathematical systems, we have pointed out the importance and place of elementary logic.

Some basic mathematical ideas

PROBLEM SOLVING

Certainly one of the major purposes of mathematics is to apply mathematics to the solution of problems. Even in the elementary grades, problem solving is important, and adds interest and understanding to the arithmetic program. Traditionally, we have placed undue emphasis on computation. Although a student may have ability in computation, he may be weak in problem solving because he lacks other abilities that are necessary in this complex process.

In the solution of problems, the student must first understand the meaning of mathematical symbols. Let us consider some examples. The numerals we use are symbols for numbers. We also have the operation symbols such as plus ($+$) for addition and times ($\times$) for multiplication. However, we have learned that the symbol ($+$) does not always mean addition. For example, in working with the integers this symbol placed before a numeral means something quite different.

Secondly, the student must develop the ability to translate a problem situation into mathematical language or symbols. Let us illustrate this ability by citing an example involving elementary algebra.

1. Suppose a farmer has one small field and one large field. The area of the larger field is 20 acres more than twice the area of the small field. The total area of both fields is 200 acres. Find the area of each field.

If we let the acreage of the small field be represented by x, then the translation of this problem into mathematical symbols is shown below.

$$(x) + (2x + 20) = 200.$$

If the student writes the sentence above for the problem, he shows that he clearly understands the condition for the problem. For some problems, several different conditions may be acceptable. But once the student writes a sentence to express a condition for the problem, he should be able to explain the condition in terms of the problem situation. The condition should correctly interpret the student's psychological understanding of the problem. Finally, the student must have the ability to process the symbols in the equation to arrive at the solution or solution set desired.

$$(x) + (2x + 20) = 200.$$

SOLUTION:

$$x + 2x + 20 = 200, \qquad \text{or} \quad \{x \mid x + 2x + 20 = 200\},$$
$$3x + 20 = 200, \qquad\qquad \{x \mid 3x + 20 = 200\},$$
$$3x = 200 - 20, \qquad\qquad \{x \mid 3x = 200 - 20\},$$
$$3x = 180, \qquad\qquad \{x \mid 3x = 180\},$$
$$x = 60. \qquad\qquad \{x \mid x = 60\},$$
$$\{x \mid x = 60\} = \{60\}.$$

Small field, 60 acres; large field, 140 acres.

You will recall from our work with equivalent conditions that each of the steps involved in obtaining the condition $x = 60$ can be justified on the basis of the field postulates. Students should be encouraged to do this from time to time to maintain their basic understanding of equivalent conditions. The obtaining of equivalent conditions should not degenerate into a mechanical process that cannot be justified on the basis of the postulates.

Problems involving rate pairs are very common in the elementary school grades. Let us consider two examples:

2. Suppose a car averages 20 miles per hour, how far will it go in 3 hours?

SOLUTION:

$$20/1 = n/3.$$
$$n = 60.$$

The one-to-one correspondence here is

$$A \{= 20, 40, 60, 80, 100, \ldots\}.$$
$$\updownarrow \ \updownarrow \ \updownarrow \ \updownarrow \ \updownarrow$$
$$B \{= 1, \ 2, \ 3, \ 4, \ 5, \ \ldots\}.$$

3. If three apples cost ten cents, what will 15 apples cost?

SOLUTION:

$$3/10 = 15/n$$
$$n = 50.$$

The one-to-one correspondence here is

$$A \{= 3, \ 6, \ 9, \ 12, 15, \ldots\}.$$
$$\updownarrow \ \updownarrow \ \updownarrow \ \updownarrow \ \updownarrow$$
$$B \{= 10, 20, 30, 40, 50, \ldots\}.$$

4. What is 15 per cent of 400?

Students should discover that problems involving per cent are actually comparison problems and are solved with greater facility and understanding when the number comparisons are symbolized by ratios. By the time students are in junior high school the following definition may be developed:

$$a/b = c/d, \text{ if and only if } ad = bc.$$

This definition can then be used to solve problems. Now let us return to our problem. The first condition is expressed below:

$$15/100 = n/400.$$

Then, we solve as follows:

$$100n = 15 \times 400.$$
$$n = \frac{15 \times 400}{100}.$$
$$n = 60.$$

CONCLUSION

Only a few areas of elementary mathematics have been covered in this book. Other topics of importance could have been included. However, if the material presented in this book is understood, the reader should find little difficulty in studying other areas of mathematics, for example, elementary geometry. Just as we encountered universes, variables, and conditions in elementary algebra, we will discover that we have universes, variables, and conditions in geometry. Whereas in algebra the universes, variables, and solution sets of conditions are sets of numbers, in geometry these ideas are associated with sets of points. In general, we might say that the approach in geometry is similar to that used for algebra.

Furthermore, we have discussed and made use of the algebra of sets. In elementary geometry we shall find that the ideas of intersection and union are frequently used to clarify basic understandings, as they were in algebra. Also, the nature of proof in geometry is basically the same as it is in algebra. Finally, after a study of elementary algebra and geometry, the step to analytical geometry is natural and comprehensible.

INDEX